Melanesia, Melancholia

and Limericks

MELANESIA, MELANCHOLIA and LIMERICKS

DAVID FLETCHER

Matador
9 Priory Business Park,
Wistow Road, Kibworth Beauchamp,
Leicestershire. LE8 0RX
Tel: 0116 279 2299
Email: books@troubador.co.uk
Web: www.troubador.co.uk/matador
Twitter: @matadorbooks

ISBN 978 1789013 214

British Library Cataloguing in Publication Data.
A catalogue record for this book is available from the British Library.

Printed and bound in the UK by TJ International, Padstow, Cornwall
Typeset in 11pt Aldine by Troubador Publishing Ltd, Leicester, UK

Matador is an imprint of Troubador Publishing Ltd

MIX
Paper from
responsible sources
FSC® C013056

For Anne and Jens

2017

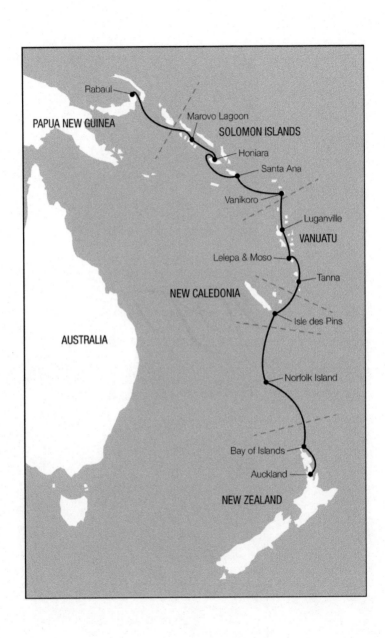

1.

*B*rian had certainly heard of Indonesia and Micronesia, and of Polynesia, Milk of Magnesia and amnesia (although he sometimes forgot this last one), but he was a little bit hazy about 'Melanesia'. So, when he saw the two-page ad for a cruise 'Across the Tropic of Capricorn' – 'taking in a mix of islands from the northernmost reaches of New Zealand to Melanesia', he had to get his atlas out.

Well, he soon had it sorted. It seems that the Pacific Ocean is split into three cultural areas: Polynesia, Micronesia and Melanesia. Polynesia, as he sort of knew, is made up of all those exotic islands scattered across the central and southern Pacific Ocean. Micronesia consists of a load of other small islands in the western part of the Pacific Ocean. And Melanesia sits to the south of Micronesia and essentially it consists of New Guinea, the Solomon Islands, Vanuatu, New Caledonia and Fiji. In other words, it's all those bits and pieces of land that lie to the north-east of Australia and stretch down in a loose chain towards New Zealand.

This, Brian found intriguing. Because, whilst he had been fortunate enough to have visited both Papua New Guinea and Fiji in the past, the Solomon Islands,

Vanuatu and New Caledonia were all places he had never been – but were the exact places that this advertised cruise would be visiting. So, would this opportunity to explore unknown destinations – and the modest size of the ship being used for the cruise – overcome his and Sandra's long-standing reluctance to participate in any sort of cruise at all?

Well, clearly the answer was 'yes'. Otherwise he wouldn't now be sitting on this bus as it made its way from Hong Kong's mega-airport into downtown Hong Kong and wondering why he and Sandra hadn't thought of a simpler way to embark on their Melanesian odyssey.

Yes. Because Melanesia is not 'just down the road' so to speak – it was always going to take some time to get there. Accordingly, the organisers of the tour, presumably aware of the average age of their punters, had sought to soften the blow of an airborne marathon by breaking the outward journey at Hong Kong for a full two nights. This would no doubt allow a mix of mature and venerable body clocks to compensate for their shift across the globe before they then had to compensate for the further shift to Auckland – where the clocks' owners would then embark on their cruise. Well, that was all very thoughtful of the organisers, but it did fail to take account of Brian's aversion to large cities and particularly to 'vibrant' large cities such as Hong Kong. He had never been here before, but only five minutes into the bus ride and he already knew he should have made other arrangements and thereby got himself and Sandra directly to Auckland. That way he wouldn't now be having to cope with the incessant commentary from the local guide at the front of the bus. That is to say, a full-volume commentary on disparate aspects of Hong Kong, delivered by a Chinese gentleman called Peter, which had commenced as soon as the bus had left the airport and which would not end until the bus had arrived at the chosen (Kowloon) hotel a full forty minutes later.

So, to start with there was a presentation on what could be seen out of the left-hand side of the bus, which was essentially an off-shore construction site of enormous proportions. And it apparently needed to be of enormous proportions because, when finished, this huge construction site would become a thirty-one-mile link between Hong Kong and Macau, the city situated on the other side of what was the Pearl River Delta. It was a stupendous undertaking, involving a series of tunnels and bridges (one as long as eighteen miles), which would ultimately tie these two conurbations together and, according to Peter, would allow all the citizens of Hong Kong to visit Macau with ease and thereby lose even more money pursuing their favourite pastime of gambling. He then made a more serious observation, that Hong Kong and Macau, together with seven other cities on the Pearl River Delta, now had a combined population of 60 million souls. And with the help of that cross-delta link, this 'PRD', already one of the most densely urbanised regions in the world, would soon become a true megacity and an even more daunting prospect for Brian than a visit to this modest settlement down the road called Hong Kong.

Brian shuddered. Hong Kong, he knew, had 'just' 7.3 million inhabitants, and all these people were squeezed into a mere 25% of this autonomous territory's land area of 427 square miles. That meant that in urban Hong Kong, the population per square mile was nearly 70,000 (compared to crowded London's 11,000). It also meant that this city might not just be 'vibrant' but also intolerably crowded. And it was.

As the really built-up parts of Hong Kong came into view, Brian could not fail to notice that it was actually built up and up and up – and up. Horizontal simply didn't feature in this cityscape. Instead there was just the vertical and then more vertical and then more vertical still. Peter seemed even quite proud of this fact, pointing out to his jet-lagged charges that with around 8,000 of the city's buildings having more than fourteen floors, Hong Kong was the 'most vertical' city in the world. Whether it was also the city with the thinnest tall buildings in the world wasn't covered, but by golly, some of those apartment blocks out there were more like slivers than blocks, and they didn't look particularly attractive places to live. In fact they looked awful places to live.

Full credit to Peter then that he confirmed this fact without being asked. Possibly because he himself was one of the majority in Hong Kong who has to attempt to bring up a family in a shoe box in the sky, where the shoe size is rarely over five or maybe not even an adult's fitting. Yes, as he went to great pains to point out, a Hong Kong family of four commonly lives in a flat of less than fifty square metres, and it can be as low as thirty square metres or, in the very worst cases, either an

4

apartment divided into cubicles or even 'cages' that can accommodate just a mattress.

Brian could simply not contemplate such an existence. Neither could he understand how urban living of this sort could be a reflection of 'progress' for mankind, and how achieving that Pearl River Delta megacity in the no doubt near future could be regarded as another leap forward in human existence. As far as he was concerned, it would just be a case of even more people crammed tightly together and inevitably more people living in people-sized rabbit hutches with just views of other rabbit hutches out of their windows. It was why he had such a distaste for cities, a distaste that grew into a horror when the city in question was so crowded and so jam-packed that it was obliged to grow ever upwards, and its citizens were obliged to accept ever more intolerable accommodation as the norm.

It's probably worth pointing out at this stage that Brian sometimes saw things from a different perspective to other people. So although he himself knew that most of his fellow bus passengers, even though exhausted from their long flight from Britain, would be relishing their transit into downtown Hong Kong, he could not keep at bay what he saw as the reality of this place. And this was its status as a human settlement, sustained by what were almost unbearable impositions on its inhabitants' existence, and probably ultimately unsustainable no matter how small the apartments are made and how many more bridges and tunnels are built to allow the inhabitants to move around.

That said, Brian did like a good joke, he felt he had

a good sense of humour, he tried not to be miserable *all* the time, and at this very moment he felt almost jubilant. And this was because his bus was pulling into the forecourt of a rather splendid-looking hotel and on one side of the forecourt was what had to be the hotel's 'pub'. And it was open.

Brian's body was still a little unsure of what time it was, but with Sandra's help and immediately after checking in, it coped with a drink and then with an evening meal and then with a short walk to observe Hong Kong's world-famous 'Symphony of Lights' – 'the biggest laser and light show in the world'. This is staged by more than forty buildings on either side of the city's bay and involves their flashing their lights in time to music while lasers are shone from their roofs. However, at the appointed time, nothing happened. Or more likely it did but at another time before Brian and Sandra had arrived to watch it. Which meant that a consolation drink was required, and in the morning they would have to seek further local entertainment in the form of a 'city tour'.

It was on another bus but with the same guide. And he hadn't got any less verbose (or any more amusing). Brian wished he'd brought earplugs. Although if he had he would have missed out on Peter's dissertation on the economy of Hong Kong and how this was based on its growing tourist industry, its international trading activities (involving the re-exporting of goods – mostly from mainland China – through its 'second busiest container port in the world') and, first and foremost, its financial services industry. He painted a glowing picture of each of these three contributors to Hong

6

Kong's prosperity, but in Brian's mind he had missed out a little of the detail. Some of the nuances of Hong Kong's enterprising ways had been omitted from the painting, and one in particular. It goes by the name of crony capitalism.

Yes. Brian had done a little research on Hong Kong before he had come here – on fun stuff like smog levels, crime rates and anti-ex-colonial sentiment – but he'd also had a glance at more serious stuff – like income inequality in the territory. This is when he'd discovered that whilst the average per capita income in Hong Kong is one of the highest in the world, the territory also suffers from some really severe income inequality – which was probably not unconnected with all those people living in shoe boxes while others drove around in one of Hong Kong's many Rolls-Royces. It was also, unquestionably, not unconnected with the fact that this teeming anthill on the coast of China is at the very top of the world's 'Crony Capitalist Index'. Which is to say that when your success as a business depends on your forming a close relationship with government officials, then Hong Kong is the place to be. Yes, if you want favours from government in the form of preferential grants or some sort of legal permit or maybe a special tax arrangement – all of which can be arranged through some of your mates in the government machine – then Hong Kong beats even Russia as the place to be, as the place to conduct the sort of business that comprehensively corrupts public-serving economic and political ideals. And strangely enough, Peter had neglected to include this fascinating fact in his presentation.

Well, it was fascinating to Brian anyway. And it just reinforced his view that Hong Kong was the sort of place he really wanted little to do with. Although, there again, as he was here it would be churlish and plain stupid not to make the most of this city tour – if only because he would never be in this city again...

So, city tour destination number one: the Peak Tram – on Hong Kong Island. This is an unmissable destination for most visitors to Hong Kong, because as well as being the first cable funicular installed in Asia (in 1888) and, as such, one of the oldest cable railroads in the world, it is also one of the steepest – and it still works! In fact it carries over 11,000 people a day – up to the Peak Tower where one can take in an incomparable view of much of the Hong Kong skyline. It was pretty impressive; both the ancient but efficient funicular and the view from the peak. However, possibly more impressive were the property prices in this elevated patch of Crowded-land.

It was Peter again, now with his charges back on the bus as it wound its way down a steep road from the peak – past a series of sumptuous-looking homes of the rich. Yes, he told them, one did need to be seriously rich to live anywhere around here. What used to be an area that the colonial British made into an exclusive residential area reserved for non-Chinese (!) had become an ultra-exclusive area for those right at the top of that income-inequality situation in Hong Kong, the only people in Hong Kong who could actually conceptualise the prices being asked for 'peak properties'. With their views, their privacy and their overt exclusivity, properties up on the peak, based on their price per square metre of living space, are now officially more expensive than those anywhere else in the world. Although, of course, one still has to stomach one's neighbours…

In describing the arrangements made by the British to keep out the locals when they chose to, Peter had been continuing a theme of 'we're pretty glad you lot have gone, because you really treated us like second-class citizens'. And whilst he was quite justified in holding these views, it did seem a little odd that he was displaying them so eagerly. Maybe that was why he eventually switched to having a go at the mainland Chinese.

It started with his telling the bus passengers that over half the visitors to Hong Kong each year are mainland Chinese. With 28 million of them pouring over the border every twelve months, they easily outnumber the visitors from all other countries combined. And they often come here for very different reasons to those of regular tourists – like to buy up Hong Kong's stocks of baby milk formula (following scandals involving food production in China itself – including the production of milk). In fact, so much baby milk formula was being snapped up that the Hong Kong authorities had to bring in limits on the number of cans of milk powder that could be taken back to China after each visit. What they couldn't do, however, was limit the disdain felt by many Hong Kong citizens for their brethren on the mainland. For not only are those naughty Chinese next door keen to get their hands on Hong Kong's milk, but they seem increasingly eager to make off with Hong Kong's residual democracy and any pretence that the principle of 'one country, two systems' is anything more than a meaningless slogan. Essentially, Hong Kong's hold on a separate political and economic system from China proper seems increasingly weak, and Peter, like many of his fellow Hong Kong citizens, was clearly not happy with what was happening. Oh, and as he was very keen to point out, most of Hong Kong's smog comes from activities in the neighbouring areas of China – but, of course, none of its urban sophistication.

What a strange situation, thought Brian. Over seven million people stacked up on a tiny patch of land, most of them having to endure all the drawbacks that come with being piled up quite so high, but still eager to defend their situation against an overwhelming threat. And that's a threat that is real in the sense of how many mainland Chinese there are and, in comparison to Hong Kong's residents, how impoverished many of them are, but also a threat that is being intensified by projects such as that Hong Kong–Macau Bridge. It's all very well to try and maintain a degree of independence while you're still Hong Kong, but it will be almost impossible to do this when you're a suburb of the Pearl River Delta megacity. Surely.

Anyway, it was shortly after this latest Brian thought that Brian's bus arrived in Aberdeen. No. Not that one, but a district on the south-west of Hong Kong Island that is famed for, amongst other things, its floating village and its floating seafood restaurants. Well, it was a change from all that vertical stuff and there was also a short boat ride – to observe all its floating attractions at close range. This was on a sampan, a vessel that was a bit like an overgrown coracle and had that same sense of

10

nobody having established which end was its front and which was its back. It didn't do much for Brian…

Never mind. Because now it was time to visit Stanley Market, another must-see in Hong Kong situated in a town called Stanley which is itself on a peninsula on Hong Kong Island. On TripAdvisor, Brian might have given the market maybe three stars (it was clean and unthreatening but free of anything he might have wanted to buy) and the seafront beyond the market might have earned itself four. Here one was able to believe that all that vertical apartment stuff had just been a dream and one could choose a cheese toastie at a seafront café by simply pointing to the sun-faded illustration of a cheese toastie on the sun-faded menu. Excellent!

Better still, it was now time to return to the hotel and, on the way, Brian could finally come to terms with why he harboured such a jaundiced view of this place called Hong Kong. It wasn't its 'vibrancy' or its overabundance of humans – or its verticality or even its social injustices and all that crony capitalism; it was the fact that, whether it liked it or not, it was part of China, and it therefore had to be condemned along with the rest of that giant country.

Yes, whilst Brian was quite sure that there were literally millions of Chinese who shared his own views on any number of issues, one could not escape the fact that China, as a society, had a number of flaws. Some of these affected only its own citizens, and were really none of Brian's business. So, if they wanted to abuse their own justice system, maintain a culture of rampant corruption or ignore the wishes of those without power, then that was their affair. But when it came to suppressing Tibetans, grabbing offshore islands for themselves in the face of international law and conducting cyberwarfare on the rest of the world, it became Brian's business as well. Oh, and then there was the little matter of their being largely responsible for the dramatic reduction in the number of elephants, tigers, rhinos, pangolins, sea cucumbers, sea horses, sharks and indeed a whole list of other endangered animals – and the likely extinction of these animals in the very near future. And no. Hong Kong could not claim it wasn't implicated. In fact, shortly before he had come away, Brian had learnt that elvers were now being poached from the River Severn and shipped to Hong Kong to feed the insatiable Chinese appetite for 'rare delicacies'. For some time they had been taken from this river – legitimately – and used to restock rivers in Europe and so build up the population of the now critically endangered European eel. However, so many were now being caught illegally – to end up on Chinese plates – that it is quite likely that Hong Kong/China will sooner or later be able to lay claim to yet another successful species extinction. Which is a fucking disgrace.

Furthermore... the assembled travellers were to be taken this evening to a Chinese restaurant for a Chinese banquet. And when Brian enquired of Peter whether said restaurant would be in the habit of offering shark fin soup to its local patrons, Peter finally conceded that it would. Whereupon, Hong Kong/Brian relations were not improved by the Hong Kong party to this exchange being informed that there was no way that an eating place implicated in the cruel and egregious liquidation of one hundred million sharks every year would be graced by the presence of the other party to the exchange and his wife. Those depraved Chinese restaurant owners could stuff their banquet, and Brian and Sandra would meanwhile indulge in an extended period of self-righteousness and what turned out to be a splendid romantic evening for two at an entirely shark fin-free hostelry within walking distance of the hotel.

All that remained to do then was to moderate the air conditioning back in their hotel room, try to get a worthwhile night's sleep, and for Brian, to ease his passage into sleep by relishing the fact that in the morning they would be leaving Hong Kong. And Peter.

And therefore he might soon bounce back to his normal cheery self...

2.

Sleeping on aeroplanes was becoming a bit of a habit. But at least on this occasion Brian and Sandra would be waking up as they approached Auckland and not Hong Kong. On top of which they would be that much nearer to Melanesia.

So Brian was in a good mood when he dropped off to sleep over the Philippines and in an even better mood when he awoke to discover that there were just two more hours in the air before they touched down in New Zealand's biggest city. It was a place that he and Sandra had visited before, and a place that they knew accommodated just a fifth of the number of people who were crammed into Hong Kong. In fact, they also knew that the whole of New Zealand accommodated barely over 60% of the number who were crammed into Hong Kong, but that sort of stuff is bordering on the nerdy and will not be referred to again. Instead, reference will be made to the less than ideal reception in Auckland. Not at its international airport but at the hotel selected for the 'cruisers'' overnight stay before they finally secured their ship. In essence, the tired, creased and crumpled cruisers arrived at this establishment at about nine o'clock in the morning, to be told that their rooms would not be available until possibly three in the afternoon. Hardly the sort of thing one would experience in Hong Kong…

Well, Brian, despite retaining his recently restored cheery demeanour, thought that this was a bit off, and he felt he should do something about it. He had no desire to linger in the hotel's lobby for six hours and neither did he want to wander the streets of Auckland before he'd had a shave and a shower. There was only one thing to do. Not to complain or make a scene. Because cheery types don't do that. But instead to ask at the hotel's reception desk whether they could possibly recommend another Auckland hotel with available rooms. Not as a ploy but as a genuine first step in securing some alternative accommodation that could be accessed immediately and not after reading *War and Peace*. Oh, and Brian made it very clear that the unavailability of rooms was not their fault but that of the organisers – and that he was fully prepared to access this alternative accommodation at his own cost.

Result! Although not the one he expected. Because the receptionist whom Brian had spoken to disappeared into an office behind reception and a little while later returned with a piece of paper – and a key to a room! There was then some whispered advice concerning the need to refrain from publicising this arrangement and the wisdom of being very discreet in extracting one's luggage from the pile of luggage near the front of the lobby. Brian was set up for a bit of covert action, but at the end of it he and Sandra would have a room and somewhere to freshen up and rest – while all their companions would be stranded in limbo. He felt more than a little guilty, but at the same time quite smug that he had achieved what others had not, but could have if they themselves had taken his own mild-mannered and pragmatic approach. Although maybe they would have needed just a little of his innate charm, a slice of his intrinsically persuasive nature and, of course, just a soupçon of his irredeemably cheery manner.

It was in the middle of this delusional episode, just as he was walking away from the reception desk, that he was greeted by one of the few fellow travellers he recognised and who recognised him. (Probably because the two of them and their respective wives had already enjoyed each other's company back in Hong Kong.) Brian even remembered his name. It was Paul – and Paul was the husband of Lydia. He was also interested in how Brian had secured a room.

Well, he hadn't even tried to extricate his luggage yet, and already he'd been rumbled. But not to worry. Paul was the only one who had noticed and he'd only noticed because he and Lydia had arranged to spend the day with a niece in Auckland and were more desperate for a room than were Brian and Sandra. Accordingly, Brian briefed Paul on the modus operandi of acquiring a room in this establishment which, when put into practice by Paul, resulted in the same outcome. Splendid! Not only did Brian and Sandra have a room, but they had now also reinforced a bond with Paul and Lydia. Conspirators together and, over the next few days, no doubt close companions too.

The same could not be said for the five people with whom Brian and Sandra shared their table at the evening's 'welcome dinner' – by which time everybody had showered and those that needed to had shaved. Two were a Swedish couple and whilst quite pleasant were still a little hard work. Two others were an English couple who were about as much fun as a funeral. And the fifth was a solo traveller who was apparently travelling light, which is why he had not bothered to bring with him any of his manners. Brian was happy when the event was over and all that remained before he got on that promised ship was a night in a bed rather than in another aeroplane and then, in the morning... another city tour.

The tour guide on this Auckland tour was also the bus driver – and a bit of a wag and a bit of an authority on Auckland house prices and how these prices were being driven skywards by the Chinese! Yes, it seemed that they either wanted to live in Auckland or acquire a property not to occupy but, through its proximity to a particular school, to secure a first-class New Zealand education for their offspring. Brian wondered how many New Zealanders were doing the same in China or Hong Kong, and took less than one second to decide that it was probably none.

Anyway, the tour was 'OK', but it had a certain flavour about it. This was the flavour of 'how can we occupy a bunch of travellers for four or five hours when all most of them want to do is get on their ship and settle down in their cabin – and have possibly only a limited interest in Antipodean conurbations?'

That said, the tour was not at all bad. It started with a gawk at rich people's houses in a posh part of town, before then delivering its participants to some sort of memorial park, the name of which Brian had forgotten before they'd left it. And before he could bring its name back to mind, the gang of literal tourists had been deposited at Auckland's Holy Trinity Cathedral. This was fairly interesting. Not only was it rather 'cool' in its design, but it had within its shadow its predecessor! This was quite novel really, but such was the affection for the earlier wooden cathedral (built in 1897) that when the new cool one came online in 1973, they moved the old one in its entirety from its old situation to within yards of its successor. And they still use it. Not quite recycling but something maybe even better…

Then it was the Auckland War Memorial Museum – which housed a Spitfire – before driving to 'North Shore', a harbourside suburb of Auckland located not surprisingly to the north of downtown Auckland, where lunch would be taken. This was good, although it did reinforce in Brian's mind just how many people he still barely recognised and how remembering names on the forthcoming cruise might prove quite a challenge.

So too was the killing of another hour at a place called Devonport before it was finally announced that the assembled party would now be driven to their awaiting ship where they would be able to board it immediately!

Well, the ship was beautiful. As was its leisurely departure from Auckland harbour. And as was their first meal on board, a meal shared with Paul and Lydia and with another delightful couple, originally from Denmark, called Thor and Lise.

So, when he went to bed that night – in a beautiful cabin – Brian was quite excited. And indisputably a lot nearer to discovering what Melanesia had in store. And, of course, what cruising had in store.

3.

 reakfast, after the first night afloat, was with one couple who were eminently pleasant and another who were more of a trial. She had little to say; he had lots to say – about model boats. Brian found him boring to the point of distressing, and he began to think that remembering everybody's name on this cruise might not be the major challenge. It might instead be avoiding all those who could cause one to start eating one's hands.

This was a serious consideration. There were eighty-eight passengers on this ship, and the eating arrangements were designed to 'get them to mix'. There were no more than a handful of tables for two in both of the ship's restaurants (of which more later) with most of the tables designed to accommodate parties of six or eight. This was not a bad thing. Indeed, it was a good thing. But it did mean that for each of the three meals every day, the first choice, on entering one of the restaurants, was with whom to sit – having within seconds decided whether an occupied table included people who might aid one's digestion or people who might impede it. After all, listening to a discourse on the control arrangements for the power unit of a model minesweeper could certainly hinder Brian's digestive process, if not put it on hold entirely.

Anyway, the discourse on model boats finally came to an end – when Brian and Sandra rose from the breakfast table – and it was now time to inspect the situation of a real boat. Or, as it is known technically, a ship. Yes, the MS *Caledonian Sky*, a proper full-sized ship, had come to rest after its overnight voyage from Auckland in a splendid place further up New Zealand's coast called the Bay of Islands. Here would take place the first excursion offered by the cruise organisers, using the vessel's fleet of ten inflatable 'Zodiacs' to ferry its passengers to shore, where they would then take in a kauri forest, a Maori concert and a visit to the famous Waitangi Treaty grounds.

Well… one of the drawbacks to getting old is that one often trips across a 'been there, done that, got the T-shirt' sort of destination. And for Brian and Sandra, the aforementioned delights had been tasted on a previous visit to New Zealand, as had a nearby place called Russell, which was advertised as a further destination in the afternoon. And as the ship was in such a delightful situation, and Brian and Sandra had not been aboard any such vessel before, and as they had yet to see any of it properly, an executive decision was made to eschew both excursions in favour of a full-blown exploration of the MS *Caledonian Sky*. This might even include some relaxed interaction with whichever other passengers were not eager to participate in every 'expedition experience' offered, either because it didn't appeal to them or because they shared Brian and Sandra's recognition of the need for an element of indolence in one's life. Especially if one had recently travelled halfway around the world.

So, the inspection of the *Caledonian Sky* got under way, and it started with an inspection of Brian and Sandra's very own part of it (at least for the next two weeks): their cabin. This was on the fifth deck of the ship (the Bridge Deck) and it was next to the chief engineer's cabin and just along from… well, the bridge. It might best be described as an exercise in wood and brass – or as a time machine, a time machine capable of whisking its occupants back to the golden days of cruising as, within it, they soaked up its ligneous opulence. There again, a little more prosaically, it could also be described as a spacious compartment panelled in brass-edged wood, complete with a large walk-in wardrobe, an even larger walk-in bathroom and, beyond a sliding glass door, a walk-out balcony. There was also a writing desk, a couple of easy chairs and an enormous bed, at the back of which was an enormous panelled mirror! Oh, and there was a telly as well. So, all in all, it was a pretty imposing place and a pretty comfortable place in which to find oneself for a fortnight at sea. So too was the rest of the ship…

Brian and Sandra embarked on their investigation of the whole ship – or at least its public parts – by returning to the restaurant where they had eaten breakfast. This was on the second deck (the Castle Deck) at its stern. It was an exercise in elegance, with more wood panelling and more brass and not surprisingly it was situated next to the ship's galley. This still left room for eleven passenger cabins towards the pointy bit of the ship along with the

22

ship doctor's accommodation and a small hospital. Brian had no plans to use this latter facility or even to exchange pleasantries with its white-suited custodian.

Moving to the deck above (the Caledonian Deck), Brian and Sandra came to the ship's main lounge. This was a very large lounge with a fireplace, a bar, a coffee station – and the air of an old people's home. It was the chairs. They were padded and quite comfy but they were all a bit too upright and they were all arranged in rows. It just didn't quite work as intended. Anyway, as one left this lounge one came to the ship's entrance hall and its reception, and beyond this space was a corridor leading to a further nineteen cabins and nothing else. It was therefore time to move to the deck above.

This fourth deck (the Promenade Deck) was essentially exclusively cabins. There were another nineteen of them here, sharing this deck with just a minute gym and an equally minute hairdresser's shop. Oh, and for the society of secret smokers there was a small open area at the stern where its members could puff away to their heart's content.

OK. Brian and Sandra were now back on their own (fifth) deck – the Bridge Deck – where there were just eight passenger cabins (including their own), the chief engineer's cabin, as already referred to, and the captain's cabin. There was also the bridge and, at the stern, on a covered but open deck, the ship's second restaurant. This was the same size as the Castle Deck restaurant, and like that restaurant, could accommodate at least most of the ship's passenger complement. Which, of course, meant that passengers could always access the restaurant of their choice – which as often as not would prove to be this second one. It seemed that an open environment in the Tropics would, very early into the voyage, constitute a much greater draw than one of elegance three decks below.

Anyway, the survey of the *Caledonian Sky* was now nearing its end because there was only one more deck to explore, the sixth deck, otherwise known as the Panorama Deck. This was where the lifeboats were stowed, which meant that it was little more than half a deck – towards the front of the ship – and it housed just the 'Panorama Lounge' and an open sun deck. The lounge was significantly more attractive than the main old people's lounge three decks below, and not only because it had a well-stocked honesty bar but also because it was tastefully furnished, it had within it an inviting little library, and forming its front was a curved bank of 'panoramic' windows. It was the sort of place where one would either want to relax indefinitely or stage an Agatha Christie murder mystery – or both.

However, relaxation and murder would have to wait because Brian had spotted in the library a tome on… what else, but the MS *Caledonian Sky* itself. So while Sandra tackled the coffee machine near the bar (a task that Brian feared and loathed in equal measure) her husband sat himself down in a comfortable chair and started to learn a little more about their seagoing conveyance.

Well, the first thing he discovered was its age. It was built in 1991 – in Italy – and since that date it had collected five previous names (including the *Megastar Capricorn*!). Of marginally more interest was the fact that it had been treated to a number of refits, the last of which was in 2011 by a firm in Great Yarmouth of all places. Anyway, moving on to its technical details, Brian established that it was 90.6 metres long with a beam of 15.3 metres and that its gross tonnage was 4,200 and its passenger and crew capacity was 189 souls. So, even though it was easily the biggest ship Brian had ever been on (if one ignored the odd ferry) it would probably be seen as nothing more than a potential lifeboat for some of the behemoth cruise ships that now put to sea. Indeed, shortly before he had come away, Brian had seen a story about the biggest cruise ship of all – visiting Southampton. This was the *Oasis of the Seas,* a vessel of 225,000 tonnes with a passenger and crew capacity of 7,800 souls (and thirty-seven bars and twenty restaurants). By Brian's calculations that meant it was like forty or fifty *Caledonian Skys* rolled into one – and how, if one was on it, one went about remembering one's fellow passengers' names was completely beyond him.

However, returning to this pocket cruise ship, Brian was fascinated to discover that it could produce forty-five tons of fresh water each day and that in the same 24-hour period it could treat twenty cubic metres of sewage – but that its top speed was just fourteen knots. There again, he thought, its passengers probably had a much greater interest in their showers and their loos working than they did in their conveyance breaking any speed records in Melanesia. And they certainly wouldn't have welcomed the idea of an additional 7,600 people on board…

Well, after an exploratory use of the honesty bar,

Brian and Sandra soon found another pair of stay-on-board passengers who agreed wholeheartedly with Brian's distaste for colossal cruise ships and their colossal number of patrons, and this was Rhona and Nouri. Together they were an example of that not so common coupling of Welsh and Iranian, and Brian had already observed their 'paced' behaviour back in Hong Kong. They were good company, and in due course, with Thor and Lise, they made the perfect companions for a memorable lunch out on that Bridge Deck restaurant. Indeed it was memorable not only because of the company but also because of the observations made by those who had returned from their morning excursion – which were now in widespread circulation. Essentially, the kauri forest had been sensational, the Waitangi Treaty grounds interesting, but the Maori concert... Well, the 'Haka' involved lots of shouting and eye-rolling from the girls, which was fine and, by common consent, a darned sight more appealing than the display of tongues by the men (which, for most of the audience, were apparently a little too furry). And if that might be interpreted as a cultural slight, then who knows what offence might be caused by some other observations that likened the authenticity of the display to that of a Stradivarius guitar.

Anyway, lunch went on far too long for quite a few and the numbers setting off for Russell were noticeably down on those who had committed themselves to Zodiac transport in the morning. This meant that there were rather more people for Brian and Sandra to meet and greet than there had been before lunch – and more of them whose names would evaporate only seconds after being revealed. It was his age, decided Brian. He had never been good at remembering names but he was now completely useless.

This maudlin self-analysis had its consequences – when Brian and Sandra finally returned to their cabin. Because Brian almost immediately became consumed with the consequences of getting old, and how so few of these consequences were in any way good.

Wisdom of sorts comes, he decided, but so too does a realisation that one is powerless, insignificant, transient, mortal and, of course, subject to a gradual or not so gradual decline which inevitably arrives before one finally expires. Basically, one loses muscle strength, agility, flexibility, resilience and stamina, and as they fade they are inevitably eclipsed by stiffness, fragility, hair loss, hair gain – where you don't want it – lots of sagging and lots of wrinkles. It's like a slowed-down film of a bowl of fresh apples, left in a warm room for a couple of weeks until they're discoloured and shrivelled. Only the apples aren't then obliged to climb stairs, pull themselves out of a bath, tip loaded wheelbarrows of garden waste or carry logs to the log burner.

There again, Brian had to admit to himself that it was possible to accommodate this physical deterioration – to a degree. One could get other people to deal with that loaded wheelbarrow, learn that grunting can assist one in rising from a seat and, most important of all, discover that the ill-advised ingestion of alcohol, whilst incapable of relieving one's aches and pains, can certainly help one in forgetting one has them. However, as well as the physical decay, there is always the possible failing of one's mental faculties, and this is by no means as simple to deal with.

In the first place one might just become 'not quite so mentally agile' or 'no longer really mentally agile at all', but at the same time just about sufficiently mentally agile to appreciate this terrible decline. Unlike those who have inadvertently raced off-piste and into the powdery snow of dementia, one might be all too aware of that downhill run, and this could clearly make life a genuine misery. Apart from anything else, one would almost inevitably realise that whilst life might not have any purpose, one's own particular life was fast approaching its end, and before one popped off one would never be able to make even the slightest dent in the affairs of the world or put to rights a single wrong amongst all those billions that afflict it. Even worse maybe is the knowledge that one would not 'live on in the minds of men' unless one was a member of that elite band of geniuses, world-shakers, tyrants and monsters whose memory is retained as some sort of eternal measure of the achievements/ abominations realised/perpetrated by those who are currently alive.

Brian was realistic enough to know that the alternative – that large bank of powdery snow – had its own drawbacks. It might just provide one with the facility to live out one's days surrounded by one's very own image of stunning alpine scenery and so avoid any recognition of the irrelevance and impotence of one's real-life existence. Or it might just furnish one with a dose of hopelessness and suffering that those still on the piste could not even begin to imagine. So either way –

on or off piste – one was in for a pretty ropy end to one's life.

Brian had all these thoughts as he was stretched out on his and Sandra's generous bed. And it was when he'd arrived at the depths of this dementia versus conscious-of-one's-decline scenario, that he realised how desolate he felt – and with no good reason. Hell, he was at the start of a fabulous cruise, lying in a beautiful cabin, with ahead of him only the prospect of good food, good company and any number of new experiences and new sights, and here he was behaving as though he'd been struck down by depression. And he hadn't been. Instead, he realised, he'd just been indulging himself in an unjustified excursion into the realms of melancholia, and it was about time he returned – to the Bay of Islands. So he did, and he did this by preparing himself for dinner. Or, more precisely, by preparing himself for the captain's dinner!

Yes, tonight was the traditional opener to any worthwhile cruise, although it would be a first for Brian and Sandra and they really had no idea what to expect. They did know, however, that the dress code was 'smart' and that proceedings would kick off in the main lounge at 6.30. So, here they sat at the appointed time with the assembled complement of passengers and with an unusually large number of the ship's own company; and before long the captain was at the front of the lounge introducing some of this company's principal players.

He started with himself, and quickly managed to demonstrate that he was a pretty approachable sort of guy and that he had not lost his native Irish accent even though he now lived in Miami. However, because he then did all the subsequent introductions – with his colleagues given only non-talking walk-on parts – nobody was able to ascertain whether his number two (the first officer) had retained his Filipino accent even though he now lived in Gloucester!

Then it was the turn of the chief engineer, a solid-looking Swede, followed by the purser (a woman) and then the 'hotel manager'. And finally there was the smiling but rather scary-looking executive chef and a guy called Garth whom Brian already recognised as the tour leader.

It wasn't made clear at this event, but in due course Brian would begin to understand how all these people and their respective subordinates fitted into the puzzle that was the ship's operation. Because the ship and the tour together required the services of three very separate teams. The first of these was the actual crew of the ship – employed by the ship's owners and led by the captain. It comprised all the guys with sailing and engineering skills and it was actually quite essential in preventing the vessel from coming to grief. The second team was under the command of the hotel manager who, with the help of the executive chef and a host of sous-chefs, waiters, barmen and cleaners, provided all the hotel services on the ship. These guys were no less than vital, and as far as Brian understood, they were employed by an enterprise that was completely independent of the ship's owners – as the ship's owners were not in the hotel business but in the ship business – obviously. That left the third (small) team, led by Garth, and he and his helpers were the representatives of the company that had organised the tour and that had chartered the ship and engaged the services of its hotel team. They couldn't operate the vessel or operate the galley or keep the ship clean, but they could operate the Zodiacs and, between them, they did have a wealth of knowledge about Melanesia's history, geography, wildlife and various cultures. Accordingly, they would be the guys who acted as the expedition's tour guides and those who organised all the on-shore visits as well as entertaining the passengers with a series of on-board presentations as the cruise progressed. Oh, and they would also ensure that the ship never ran out of unbounded enthusiasm, and in this respect, Garth would prove to be the unsurpassed master. He would reveal that his own enthusiasm wasn't just unbounded but also incredibly intense. Indeed frighteningly intense. And certainly irrepressible.

Anyway, he wouldn't have an opportunity to parade his fervour this evening because the captain's introductions had now been completed and so too had his welcoming remarks, and it was therefore time to troop down to the Castle Deck restaurant for the captain's dinner itself. Here Brian and Sandra ended up on a table with four others, all of whom were retired but two of whom had been a married pair of GPs. They were now a married pair of retired GPs, and as they looked as though they were amongst the youngest passengers aboard the ship, Brian wondered whether the NHS was possibly on the point of running out of GPs entirely.

However, notwithstanding the imminent collapse of the National Health Service, ultimately it was time for bed. Yes, it was time for Brian and Sandra to climb up three decks whilst, at the same time, rejoicing in the fact that, despite their age-related downward incline, neither of them even considered using the *Caledonian Sky's* available lift.

And both of them could still count backwards from fifty...

4.

ell, for both Brian and Sandra, today would be a first. It would be the first day of their lives where they would not see land. And not because they would be keeping their eyes closed all day, but because they were on a ship steaming north from New Zealand, and north of New Zealand there is no land to see. Instead one has just a large expanse of water called the Tasman Sea, otherwise known as 'The Ditch', and, like all expanses of sea, this Ditch is pretty well featureless and, for very many people, not entirely engrossing. Which is why, soon after breakfast, there was a presentation in the principal lounge entitled 'A life on the ocean waves – seabirds of the Pacific'.

This would mark the start of a whole series of on-board presentations and lectures designed to inform and distract the ship's passengers, and it would be presented by the ornithologist in Garth's team, a gentleman who proved to be very knowledgeable about seabirds of the Pacific but not quite so au fait with what was an appropriate length for his shorts. They were simply far too long, and with his short-statured body, made him look a little like a hobbit. Brian advised his wife of this observation soon after the presentation had begun, and soon after this his wife advised him that he should get out of the habit of identifying every opportunity to be mean about people and instead relish the fact that he was being spoon-fed information. He wasn't even having to open a book to learn about the local pelagic wildlife. Instead, he could just sit in this old people's lounge on a comfy chair and have the whole lot delivered to him intravenously and without any effort whatsoever.

Well, Brian felt suitably chastised, and it wasn't until later that it became apparent that Sandra's enthusiasm for attending on-board presentations didn't preclude a successful challenge to that rather pointed 'no effort whatsoever' element of her rebuke. It was when they were both back in their cabin after their ornithological enlightenment and while the crew were occupied in simulating a bomb search (!) – and specifically when Brian was investigating their in-cabin telly. He had soon discovered that it had on offer a small number of channels. Two of these carried rolling news programmes, a further four, a selection of films, 'nature programmes' and other equally missable diversions (but no porno stuff) and one channel relayed the audio content of those lounge presentations, together with whatever visual aids were being used by the presenter. So, essentially, one could 'attend' an on-board exposition without even making the effort to walk to the ship's lounge. Instead, one could sit on one's bed and tune in.

Well, neither Brian nor Sandra would admit to being the instigator, but when, at 11.30, Garth's resident historian embarked on a presentation entitled 'Off the Map: a Brief History of Pacific Charts, Part One', two of his audience were not there in person to hear it. Instead, they were on their bed in their cabin, dividing their time between ascribing their idleness to residual jet lag and forming the opinion that Captain Cook certainly did get around a bit...

Yes, as soon became apparent, in discussing the history of Pacific charts, one cannot avoid discussing Captain Cook and his cartographic habits. For here was a man who, having made detailed maps of Newfoundland, sailed off south a bit and made not just one and not just two but three voyages around the Pacific. In performing this remarkable feat, he achieved, amongst other things, the first recorded contact by a European with the coastline of Australia and the first recorded circumnavigation of New Zealand. He also, of course, mapped huge formerly uncharted areas of the globe – and his excursions took him to Norfolk Island, New Caledonia and Vanuatu, all places that Brian and Sandra would soon be visiting themselves.

He also provided pub quizzers with that tricky, not to say testing, question, which is: 'On which of his three Pacific voyages did Captain Cook get killed?' Fortunately, Brian knew the answer to this one. It was his third voyage, which was when he upset a few Hawaiians and got himself excused all duties – permanently. There again, the Hawaiians did look after him once he was dead, preparing his body for the afterlife in the same way that they prepared the bodies of their own chiefs and other bigwigs. That is to say, they disembowelled him, baked him to facilitate the removal of flesh and then cleaned his bones in order to be able to return them to his colleagues for burial at sea. So, all in all, no hard feelings on either side.

Returning to the lecture... Brian was interested to hear that the first recorded circumnavigation of the world by a non-human animal was by Captain Cook's goat, who made this incredible journey on two separate occasions. She was eventually put out to pasture on Cook's farm back in England and died in 1772 – and there is apparently no truth in the rumour that in her retirement years she was renamed Vas-goat da Gama. Well, this was just the sort of essentially useless but fascinating information that Brian would be able to recall well into his dotage, when even remembering which day of the week it was would be a trial. Indeed, it was in that same category of pointless knowledge that included the fact that Captain Cook was keen on limericks. They apparently kept his crew happy on his long voyages and that was a very good thing. And the cruder and the dirtier the limerick, the better it worked for his men. As it did for Brian, come to that...

Anyway, the lecture on charts and Captain Cook eventually drew to a close and Brian and Sandra then managed to walk the forty metres from their cabin to the outside restaurant and there participate in a pleasant lunch. After this it was time for the third lecture of the day, this one entitled 'The lonely little outpost – an introduction to Norfolk Island'. Well, this one was guaranteed to spark the idlers' interest – and their attendance in person in the lounge – because it was advertised as a comprehensive introduction to that tiny dot in the ocean that they would be visiting tomorrow, and about which their current level of knowledge might be described as 'equally tiny'.

So, at three o'clock they were sitting in the lounge with a good few other passengers, and ready to be extracted from their state of ignorance about this remotest of islands.

This extraction process began with the presenter (another member of Garth's team who unfortunately put Brian in mind of Liam Byrne) providing his audience with the information that Norfolk Island is a full 900 miles east of Australia and, on its fourteen square miles of land, it hosts just under 1,800 people, none of whom, as far as he was aware, commuted to the mainland to work. To do that, he suggested, would probably require the services of an intercontinental ballistic missile and would therefore be both unaffordable and possibly dangerous.

Then it was history time, and this kicked off with the information that Norfolk Island was first settled by a few Polynesians back in the thirteenth and fourteenth centuries, but that they didn't stay long and they were definitely not responsible for the island's current name. That was all down to the star of the previous lecture on charting the Pacific, none other than the famous Captain Cook (on his second voyage). Because, having sighted it in 1774, he named it Norfolk Island after Mary Howard, Duchess of Norfolk – unaware (as she hadn't opened a Twitter account) that she had actually died since he and his crew had shipped off from England. So it may rank as one of the few islands in the whole world named after a corpse. Brian wasn't really sure and the presenter didn't comment.

Anyway, it was now a British possession, and it didn't take us too long to work out how we might usefully employ fourteen square miles of land lying 900 miles off the Australian coast. Which is why, in 1788, we established a penal settlement on the island, which remained there until 1855 – except for an eleven-year hiatus between 1814 and 1825 when it was abandoned, reputedly because the head warder had lost the keys and couldn't lock anybody up until he'd eventually got a locksmith in to sort it all out – in 1825. Brian could well understand that. He'd had the same sort of trouble when he'd lost his keys to the barn...

So, moving on from the plain ridiculous to the plain facts, Brian and Sandra learnt that pretty early on in its days as a penal colony, Norfolk Island was regarded as being just too remote as well as being too difficult for shipping (there are no natural moorings on the island) and too costly to maintain. So in 1814 it was closed down for a rather more rational reason than lost keys and the prison buildings were actually torn down, so as not to serve as an inducement to settlers from other countries, and particularly to those from other countries in Europe. Of course, this meant that when the island was brought back into service in 1825 to serve as a place to send 'the worst description of convicts', there was a bit of rebuilding to undertake. And one has to question why they bothered, because the new settlement didn't take 'the worst description of convicts', but instead just men who had committed fairly petty property crimes, often earning them no more than three years in clink. And then, of course, the whole thing was wound up again just thirty years later (probably without much of a fanfare back home in order to avoid accusations that the government of the day was suffering from another case of penal dysfunction...).

Well, whatever the wisdom of establishing and then re-establishing a prison on Norfolk Island, in 1855 it was now an empty island – but not for long. Yes, just when it thought it might finally be free of those pesky humans, along came some of the descendants of the HMS *Bounty* mutineers, including those of Fletcher Christian himself. It appears that with their Tahitian partners, those original mutineers had set in train a reproductive habit that would eventually see their progeny outgrowing their Pitcairn Island home, and consequently give rise to a need to relocate some of their number to that other island down the road, the conveniently situated and free of current tenants, Norfolk Island.

Just under 200 of them came. They quickly occupied the prison buildings and then they set about providing for themselves by pursuing a mix of traditional farming and, regrettably, traditional whaling. And much to the relief of all the whales in the world, who now only have to worry about seagoing vessels from Iceland, Norway and Japan, those new colonists have long since abandoned whaling and now just occupy themselves with farming – and a bit of tourism – and a bit of anti-Australian sentiment...

Yes, the presenter had informed his audience that in 1979, Norfolk Island, which was part of the settlement of Australia, had been granted limited self-government by Australia. This led to the formation of a Norfolk Island Legislative Assembly and, within the population, a sense that they could now get on with running their own affairs. This they did – until 2006, when they were forced to look to the Federal Government for financial assistance. This had consequences, and in 2015 Norfolk Island's very much bigger brother decided to replace the Assembly with an Administrator and an advisory council. That is to say that from that date Norfolk Island became a territory of Australia, bound by most of the Australian Commonwealth laws and having to comply with the same taxation, social security, immigration, customs and health arrangements as apply on mainland Australia. (And flights between Norfolk Island and Australia switched from being international flights to domestic flights overnight.)

These new arrangements were imposed against the will of the majority of Norfolk Islanders, who inevitably objected to their 'recolonisation' by those buggers from overseas. Even if those buggers had bailed them out and now continued to support them. And so, even in this remotest corner of the populated world, discord abounds and resentment simmers. It seems, thought Brian as he listened to this particular aspect of the lecture, that mankind can conjure up disharmony, strife and even hostility in the unlikeliest of places and with a facility that is unsurpassed by any other species. How long would it take, he pondered, for the well-behaved, reasonably-minded passengers on this ship to form into cliques, for those cliques to become factions and then for those factions to identify any number of reasons to fall out with other factions and thereby set in motion a process that would lead to friction, antagonism and open enmity? Jeez, by the end of this voyage there could be mayhem: multiple hernias, outbreaks of angina and even seriously kicked shins. Or maybe it would follow the Norfolk Island approach to violent rebellion, which was to form a Norfolk Island People for Democracy movement, and appeal to the United Nations to include the island on its list of 'non-self-governing territories'. And see how Australia likes that! Yes, concluded Brian, we manage to propagate conflict everywhere, but in some parts of the world we are at least able to manage this conflict in a non-violent and civilised manner. So in fact there was as much likelihood that bullets and bombs would make an appearance on Norfolk Island as would… hernias and kicked shins on the *Caledonian Sky*. For which fact Brian was truly thankful.

He was also thankful that the lecture on Norfolk Island had eventually drawn to a close. It had been interesting but not that interesting, and he'd also had enough of the rather peculiar atmosphere of the lounge. He wanted to swap it for the atmosphere of an inviting cabin. So, within just a couple of minutes of learning a final piece of trivia about Norfolk Island – that Helen Reddy had a home there – Brian was back in his cabin. More accurately he was sitting on a chair on the cabin balcony, looking at the Tasman Sea, while Sandra, on another chair on the balcony, was reading a book. And it wasn't long before he was feeling really desolate again, not this time through his thinking about getting old but through his considering the phenomenon of waning friendships…

It was not what he wanted, but he just couldn't

stop himself engaging with this depressing topic – and analysing what actually happens. And his analysis started with a harmless review of how virtually everybody maintains a 'circle of friends', a group of people with whom they have a bond of mutual affection and with whom they seek to socialise or at least keep in contact. However, this circle is not immutable. It is 'dynamic' in the sense that as one goes through life and one makes one's way from school to university and then to work, say – or to a different town or to a different country maybe – some friendships are inevitably abandoned, new friendships are formed and sometimes old friendships are revived. This process is natural and can be readily coped with. Indeed if one didn't constantly discard friendships during a lifetime and simply went on adding more, one would end up with an unmanageable number of relationships and one would have to start writing Christmas cards in July.

This was where Brian's thoughts turned to the maudlin. Because he now began to consider how, within this 'dynamic' operation of friendships, some of them become indisputably long-standing, and these are generally the friendships that are cherished above all others. Which is why, when *they* 'sour', it can be a cause for real anguish – and why, just thinking about this almost unavoidable aspect of long-standing friendships can spawn the sort of melancholia by which he had now been overtaken. And this aspect of long-standing friendships *is* almost unavoidable. He was convinced of it. And he was convinced of it because he knew that over the long life of such a friendship, both parties to the friendship change. That happy-go-lucky guy whom you got drunk with in your twenties is now an uptight arsehole with uptight habits and is about as much fun as a stomach ulcer – while you're still an unreformed pisshead who thinks euthanasia through bingeing on Pernod is not only feasible but also a pretty attractive way to go. Interests diverge as well. You want to discuss the failings of Homo sapiens and how, all on its own, this one species is visiting an apocalypse on the world – or maybe just touch on the genius of Neil Innes – and he no longer wants to talk about either of these things but instead is rather more interested in *Holby City* and *EastEnders*, or the unremarkable academic achievements of an unremarkable daughter or son, or possibly the wonders of the latest mind-mushing app that he's found.

It gets worse, thought Brian. Long-standing friendships can also develop 'asymmetry'. So whenever you see that friend, you ask about him and what he is doing, and he responds – at length – but he rarely reciprocates and can happily leave you not knowing whether you have just won the Nobel Prize for Literature or just lost your house as a result of a moment of madness in Las Vegas. He probably wouldn't even know that you'd been to Las Vegas, even though you knew where he'd been every week for the last three months because he'd spent the last half an hour showing you a parade of photos on his bastard smartphone.

So, Brian concluded, long-standing friendships are set up to disappoint. And few of them disappoint – in disappointing. It was probably why so many people eventually became recluses, he thought, and it was definitely why Brian felt so miserable as he gazed out over the sunlit waters of the vast Tasman Sea.

What was wrong with him!? Why in heaven's name was he indulging in this further bout of unjustified misery? And what could he do about it?

Well, he really had no idea why he'd succumbed to such nonsense, but when he'd shaken off the remnants of his thoughts on deteriorating friendships, he did have an idea of how he might prevent this nonsense from returning. It was simple. He'd do what Captain Cook's sailors had done. He'd set about composing some crude limericks. If they'd worked to keep those blokes happy while aboard their vessel for months, then they would probably work for the two short weeks that Brian was at sea. And what better time to start this remedy than now? Before it was time to report for the evening briefing and before Brian questioned the wisdom of his somewhat ludicrous therapy for melancholia.

It took him a full hour to compose his first limerick. Then it was time for that briefing. This was the daily event held in the main lounge just before dinner, the purpose of which was to allow Garth to give a short report on the day's events – if there had been any – but more importantly to give his audience a brief rundown of what they could expect the next day, together with any necessary warnings or cautions. Well, on this occasion the briefing resolved itself into a confirmation that the visit to Norfolk Island would take place as planned and that because of the forecast state of the sea and the absence of any usable harbour facilities on the island, initiating the visit in terms of landing on the island would be something of a challenge…

Well, Brian tried to assess whether this disconcerting news together with his limerick composition had seen off any residual melancholia for today, but could only conclude that at least he had an appetite for dinner and a desire to share this dinner with the 'friendly four': Thor and Lise and Paul and Lydia. This he succeeded in doing – by making an early exit from the lounge with Sandra and securing a table for six in the Bridge Deck restaurant and then guarding it until the foursome arrived. They were then able to enjoy a memorable meal together, one marred only by Brian insisting that his companions hear his ideas for some much-needed remedial work on the British democracy. He started his address by making clear that democracy as practised in the UK, although a model for the rest of the world, was no more than a distortion of real democracy and almost beyond redemption. However, he went on to explain, it could be improved marginally if we took some steps to recognise the obvious inequities in the electoral process. Why, he asked, should a tenth-generation Englishman who has maybe served in the armed forces and now, in his later life, devotes himself to charitable work, be granted no more voting power than somebody who has been sent a British passport through the post, and whose English isn't up to explaining that her husband actually votes on her behalf anyway.

Well, Sandra could see where this was going. She'd heard his ideas on being 'licensed to vote' before. So she headed him off at the pass by suggesting that he switched from his ideas on British democracy to his scheme for generating power from harnessing the spin of the Earth. This did the job perfectly and nobody was offended – or indeed enlightened a great deal. Unfortunately, she had no similar remedy for the announcement her husband made when they were back in their cabin. Because it was now time for Brian to disclose to Sandra that he had this excellent plan to pen a whole succession of limericks during the course of their trip – and that he was now ready to reveal the very first result of this plan.

In response to the news that her husband was to devote his previously hidden poetic prowess to the construction of any number of 'five lines of filth', Sandra could only provide her husband with some advice. This was in the form of a question and the question was 'Why don't you grow up?' Brian didn't furnish her with an answer to this question, but instead cleared his throat and then read out his first limerick. Without any adequate warning and without any hint of embarrassment whatsoever. It was:

Young Jack with the help of a friend
Would a brick from his penis suspend
His ambition, you see
Was not one brick but three
And… he did pull it off in the end

Her response to this was not any further advice but a sort of disgusted snort. Brian wasn't unduly surprised, because, as was all too obvious, Sandra wasn't a burly mariner for whom such poetic offerings were designed. Whereas… he thought, there would be a whole island full of these types tomorrow, the no doubt strapping descendants of Fletcher Christian and his chums who probably still made up mucky limericks to this day. Which meant there was no doubt about it. When on Norfolk Island tomorrow, he'd present his limerick number one – to an appreciative audience. And if it went down as well as he knew it would, it would then give him the stimulus and the confidence to go on to produce many more of them and thereby keep in check that threatening melancholia.

Yes. It seemed that as he got older he got no less delusional and possibly even more so...

5.

*B*rian had experienced a disturbed night. He'd found himself involved in Brexit. Indeed, very involved, in that he was leading the Brexit negotiations for Britain and was having to deal with the EU's spiv-in-chief, the delightful and not in the least bit unreasonable Jean-Claude Juncker. And things weren't going well. Not only was Jean-Claude not being his normal genial self, but he was being uncharacteristically demanding as well. He wanted billions of pounds to cover his personal pension costs and he wanted a force field built between the Irish Republic and Northern Ireland. Brian was obliged to become resolute in his response – and imaginative in his response. Which is why he suggested that Mr Juncker could have his billions if he took them not in cash but in kind – and specifically in the form of Northern Ireland. This province, Brian argued, was worth quite a few billions, even with its sitting tenants. And furthermore, if the EU took it in settlement of their financial demands, it would even obviate the need for that force field. They could just lump it together with the Republic of Ireland, and everybody would be happy. Or at least, a lot of people would be happy. Unfortunately, Mr J was having none of it and became so rude that Brian was obliged to punch him on the nose. After that the dream became even more disturbing. This was when Tony Blair arrived – to put in an offer for Northern Ireland himself, with the intention of turning it into a retirement home for ex-J P Morgan bankers. Well, dreams can be really disturbing and really peculiar. But not that peculiar. Which is why Brian sought out another nightmare experience and ended up finding one that featured a clean-shaven Jeremy Corbyn playing a pretty incoherent and very left-wing Freddy Krueger. Not surprisingly, Brian was mightily relieved when he finally awoke. Particularly because he recalled almost immediately that he had a really exciting day to look forward to: a day on Norfolk Island.

Shortly after breakfast it started – with some bureaucracy. Yes, Norfolk Island, as previously explained, is part of Australia, and Australia properly protects its borders. Which is why Brian and Sandra found themselves standing in a queue in the main lounge waiting to be processed by two Australian border officials who had been shipped in on a Zodiac and were now inspecting an assembled collection of passports as their owners filed past. After all, what could be an easier backdoor route into Australia than waiting until one was at least middle-aged and then booking an expensive cruise with the aim of slipping into one of its offshore islands a mere 900 miles off its coast? When Brian vocalised these thoughts to his wife, she told him to zip it and just smile at the officials as if they were some long-lost friends. And in that way, she and her husband soon found themselves cleared to enter Australia and cleared initially to enter a Zodiac. This was the third of the Zodiacs to set out from the ship towards Norfolk Island and the third to be put to the test of landing on this island. Because, just as advised, this landing looked as though it could be quite a challenge.

There was just a jetty, and this jetty was on the other side of some 'lively seas' and it was being besieged by a series of 'lively swells'. It simply wasn't the sort of place that one would chose to land a squadron of marines, let alone a bunch of 'seniors', but it appeared that it was the only place there was – and it was already in use. For as Brian and Sandra bobbed around on their approach to the island, they could see that the first Zodiac was already being unloaded. As theirs got closer, the second was being dealt with – by its eight occupants being literally manhandled to ensure that they landed on some steps to the jetty and not in the sea. Then it was their turn.

It was a little like trying to exit a lift at House of Fraser, where, because of the hacking of the lift's software, the lift itself is oscillating vertically at the entrance to the 'women's fashions and haberdashery floor', and any successful purchase of a new fascinator and a replacement zip for Jonny's chinos is going to involve a rather too literal leap of faith. Oh, and worse still, there was lots of water around, not just in the heaving sea, but on the steps of the jetty and on that flat bit at their foot where one was supposed to dismount. Well, with the helping hands of Garth and two of his assistants, the impossible was achieved and Brian found himself duly landed and in a dry enough position to now relish the forthcoming landing of his wife. She was the last of the eight on this third Zodiac to leave it and nearly the first to come to grief through the agency of a particularly large swell. But she made it, and that meant there were now only seven more Zodiacs to be unloaded in the same slow, cumbersome fashion. As was becoming very obvious very quickly, the transferring of passengers from the *Caledonian Sky* to terra firma was never going to be as expeditious as the landing of that earlier mentioned squadron of marines. Or indeed the landing of an entire regiment of marines – on a dark night onto a beach covered in particularly thick treacle…

Anyway, Brian and Sandra now had time to inspect their surroundings. These consisted of the short jetty on which they were standing, a surfaced area beyond this on which were parked three buses (!), a series of stone buildings beyond these vehicles, and framing these nearer features, a park-like landscape dotted with pines.

Well, Brian now recalled what he'd learnt in his Norfolk Island lecture of the previous day. That when a cargo ship arrives at Norfolk Island, it moors out at sea – just as the *Caledonian Sky* had – and it is emptied by its contents being transferred, five tonnes at a time, into whaleboats, which are then towed to this jetty. Unless, of course, the sea is even rougher than it was today, in which case the ship will relocate to the other side of the island and try its luck at Norfolk Island's other diminutive jetty. And presumably, if that fails, it just buggers off and, with a small 'we called' printed card, advises the Norfolk Islanders to collect their goodies from the not-so-local depot any time between 8am and 5pm – at their own convenience. 'And sorry we missed you'.

Then there were those stone buildings. They were the remains of the Norfolk Island prison – with some later additions – and some of them were now being used by the authorities as administrative offices and the like, and accordingly they looked very neat and tidy. In fact, that landscape beyond them looked very neat and tidy as well, and when Brian and Sandra finally began to move through it – on one of those buses – it became apparent that it was *exceedingly* neat and tidy, as indeed was the whole of Norfolk Island. The *Caledonian Sky* had, it seemed, delivered its complement of passengers to a comprehensively manicured dot in the Pacific like no other remote dot that Brian and Sandra had ever been to before.

Yes, with all the Zodiacs relieved of their cargo and the cargo stowed onto those three buses, the exploration of Norfolk Island had commenced at a sensible speed along a paved road. And this road ran through closely cropped grass, populated by the numerous cows who kept it cropped, and studded here and there with the not quite so numerous Norfolk Island pines – which define this small territory, and even feature on its flag.

Well, this was all very nice, if not very exciting, but it inevitably reminded Brian of what this island had once been: a small patch of land covered in forest, including stands of pristine subtropical rainforests. As well as this assemblage of unique flora, it also, of course, had its own unique fauna, most of which if not now extinct is very rare or seriously threatened. With our farming practices and with the help of herds of ruminants, we may have tidied this place up, thought Brian, but that tidying process has involved our obliterating most of what was once here. This meant that most of the endemic species of plants are either on the edge or literally on the edge, as on a few stretches of inaccessible clifftops. Or maybe they are corralled into the Norfolk Island National Park, the small tract of rainforest that hasn't been cleared for grazing or housing and represents the last place on the island where introduced weed species don't outnumber the island's native species. And it's even worse when one examines the island's fauna, which of course Brian wasted no time in doing…

Yes, the endemic animals of Norfolk Island simply got steamrollered, either by the removal of their habitat or by the impact of introduced species. And if they survived that onslaught, then they were still likely to succumb to the practice of hunting. Which is why, if we ever want to see a Norfolk Kaka (a beautiful large parrot), we will have to make do with a visit to Birmingham Museum where they house a stuffed one. And if we want to make the acquaintance of the sublime Norfolk ground dove, we will have to inspect the single illustration of this lost bird made by a guy called John Hunter in a book he produced in the late eighteenth century and without which we would probably not even be aware that it once existed and that it has now been lost forever.

God, this was just like Hong Kong, thought Brian. While most of the other passengers on his bus were soaking up the delights of a new environment, here he was wallowing in everything that was wrong about it, even if all those wrongs were long past and all of them were no less than inevitable. It's just what happens, he admitted to himself. People arrive in an untouched environment and they cannot fail to touch it. They certainly don't just sit around and admire the scenery and the wildlife – while they starve to death – but instead they take whatever steps are necessary to ensure their survival, even if it means that not much of anything else survives. It's what we've been doing as a species for millennia, all around the globe. But even so, he thought, why do we have to be quite so rapacious? Why is there not just a little dose of forbearance in our nature, especially when that forbearance would entail our leaving alone such a tiny and such a precious part of our planet, a minuscule island that we could well do without – for our own purposes – and that even now cannot properly sustain its human burden?

Shit, Brian needed a distraction, and within only a few minutes, one arrived. It was in the form of St Barnabas Chapel. The three buses had now stopped and were disgorging their passengers at the entrance to a small church situated in open countryside. Brian's immediate thought was that if the intention was to go inside this church, then, taking account of that visit to Auckland's cathedral just three days before, his dealings with places of worship would experience a spike like they had never done before and were unlikely ever to do again. His less immediate thought was that this chapel place looked very attractive and it was probably very well worth a proper look at – inside as well as outside.

It was. It was as beautiful inside as it was handsome

without. And it had a great history, having been built originally for the Melanesian (!) Mission, whose school and headquarters were based on Norfolk Island for over fifty years up until 1920. It was actually established as a memorial to a chap called John Coleridge Patteson, who had been ordained as the Bishop of Melanesia in 1861 but who was subsequently killed as the Bishop of Melanesia as a result of a misunderstanding in the Solomons...

This information, and a lot of other stuff about the church, was provided by a thick-set Norfolk Islander. He was apparently a direct descendant of those *Bounty* mutineers from the past and he most certainly looked the part. He was clearly not to be messed with. Just as clearly as he was not to be challenged on his knowledge of St Barnabas Chapel, which included the revelation that amongst its many notable features were marble tiles from Devon, kauri pews from New Zealand, a roof of Norfolk pine from... Norfolk Island – and windows that were the work of William Morris and Sir Edward Burne-Jones! These fenestrations, decided Brian, must have constituted the most valuable artefacts on the island – and were probably worth, on their own, a great deal more than the entire property that the collected 'Caledonians' would next visit.

This was a private house owned, it transpired, by the same guy who owned the buses. In this way he could probably extract not just a bus-hiring fee from the tour organisers, but a further fee for serving late morning tea and cake to their assembled travellers. He may even have charged a premium for his drivers furnishing these travellers – when they were back on the buses – with the information that one can list one's nickname in the island's phone directory. This apparently is allowed because, with so many of the island's inhabitants being descended from the Pitcairn Islanders, distinct surnames are in short supply, and a phonebook full of the equivalents of just Smith, Jones and Brown would not be very useful. Accordingly, one can find in this publication such characters as Goof, Rubber Duck, Diddles and Tarzan. But apparently no Cobber and no Sheila. Oh, and Goof and his friends may well speak a local creole language as well as English. This is a blend of eighteenth century English and Tahitian and it is known as Norfuk. Honestly.

Anyway, the buses had now made their way through a street with shops on either side, which apparently constituted the island's capital, and they had delivered their contents to a picnic spot where lunch was to be served. This proved to be a tasty highlight of the visit and, with its mix of local delicacies such as 'sweet-lipped fish' and local concoctions such as banana 'bread' and coconut bread, it was marginally more interesting than the subsequent visit to the aforementioned Norfolk Island National Park. Brian and Sandra had chosen this excursion – while others went off to tour either the convict settlement or the island's botanical gardens – and first discovered that it was on the highest point of the island, otherwise known as Mount Bates. They then discovered that it was essentially deficient in birds but very soon well supplied with rain. Brian was not alone in being quite relieved to be back on the bus.

When the bus then arrived at the jetty, he was further relieved to see that the sea was no longer in a strop. This meant that the return trip to the *Caledonian Sky* would be less of a challenge than this morning's nautical undertaking. It also meant that Brian would soon be back on board his floating home without having presented his first limerick to a single Norfolk Islander as he'd intended. But there just hadn't been the opportunity. Whereas... back on the ship there would be the immediate opportunity to begin the process of distilling his experience of Norfolk Island. Which, for this irredeemable curmudgeon, meant that he would now be able to get on with condensing his earlier thoughts on the transformation of Norfolk Island by man into a bout of some serious, heavy-duty melancholia concerning... trees.

Yes, what he'd seen on Norfolk Island – a place famed for its Norfolk Island pines – had really got him thinking about trees and about what we, as a species, do to trees and indeed to all sorts of defenceless flora all over the world. Sometimes it's a matter of plunder: our violating a once pristine forest, say, in order to cut down and drag out its most venerable and beautiful trees. Or more often it is simply a matter of clearance. That land that the vegetation is occupying is wanted for another purpose. It needs to be cut down, burnt down or grubbed out, so that in its place can be grown flax, soya, corn, beef or houses. And so it was in Norfolk Island. Having cut down the taller pines to discover that they didn't work as ships' masts, we then cleared virtually the whole island to allow no more than a handful of Homo sapiens to exist somewhere that they probably should never have existed.

Yes, Brian thought, for a species whose ancestors lived their lives in trees and many of whose modern cousins still do, we have a very casual attitude to the treatment of these natural wonders and, indeed, to all forms of vegetation. We now rape and clear forests on an industrial scale, but as these forests consist of lifeforms without blood and without a voice with which they can scream, too few people *really* care. After all, it's not like bludgeoning to death dolphins or machine-gunning bison. It's just chopping down 'stuff'. And anyway, we've all done that. In fact, it's so ingrained in the human consciousness – this imperative to 'clear a space', whether for living in or living off – that few of us have any compunction in uprooting an unwanted tree in our garden or maybe lopping off its limbs in the best traditions of butchered beauty. And so the devastation of plant life goes on unabated, and will go on unabated, because unlike areas of virgin forest which are fast disappearing, our species is doing just the opposite, and therefore there will be that imperative to clear a space until there is nothing more to clear. Until natural flora is as rare as real empathy for anything that grows in the ground.

Brian found this disregard for all plant life really depressing. Not just because he knew that it had a terrible impact on all those animals that depended on it – like orangutans, tapirs, gibbons, fruit bats and the odd four million other forest-living species – but because it once again betrayed mankind's belief in its own importance and the insignificance of everything else. If we were the principals in the play of life, then we might just concede that a few animals could have a couple of walk-on parts or maybe one or two subordinate roles – if they were iconic, cute or tasty enough. But plant life... well, it rarely featured even as a prop, and if it was acknowledged at all then it would be as a piece of dimly lit scenery, something of no consequence – to be rearranged, torn down, discarded or made into something else as we chose.

If only trees could fight back. If only Tolkien's Ents really existed and could mobilise whole forests. And if only the moon was made of cheese. Yes, this was deep into no-hope territory and Brian knew it. He felt more depressed than ever.

There was only one thing to do: compose a limerick. And that's exactly what he did. Only he didn't manage just one. He managed two. And then he managed not to reveal them until after another fine dinner, when he and Sandra were back in their cabin and tucked up in bed. Then he did. And they were as follows:

There was a young actor from Derby
Who just knew that one day he'd a star be
But his dreams came to nought
When one day he was caught
With a full-sized inflatable Barbie

And

There was a young girl who was found
At the top of a hill on the ground
It seems that a youth

(Who was very uncouth)
Had intended to get on her mound

Sandra was… unimpressed. She didn't say so, but her expression said it all. And Brian began to wonder whether his antidote to melancholia might itself prove another source of… melancholia. It was just as well that he was pretty well impervious to rational thinking when he had a bit between his teeth – and scores of further limericks to compose and then present. Hell, he hadn't even composed a worthy limerick about Jean-Claude Juncker yet – and neither had he produced an ode that the sailors on the *Bounty* would have considered even marginally filthy.

So, sorry Sandra, but prepare to be unimpressed again – and again – and again…

It's called being married.

6.

reakfast was with a pair of travellers from Glasgow by the name of Gill and Vic, and it involved red-billed tropic birds, fairy terns and slender-billed white-eyes. These tropical birds weren't, of course, on the menu, but they had all been seen on yesterday's visit to Norfolk Island and were now being recalled by Sandra as she chatted to the Scots. She was telling them that she had been particularly pleased to see the pair of fairy terns – in a tree next to St Barnabas Chapel – and gratified to have clocked a couple of slender-billed white-eyes, one of the few birds endemic to Norfolk Island and therefore a bird that was under threat. Brian kept out of this exchange. He could ill afford to be reminded of the desperate circumstances of most of Norfolk Island's fauna – and its flora – and had promised himself that today he would be just a tad more upbeat. And with it being yet another day entirely 'at sea' he thought he might just manage this, helped no doubt by an imminent, uplifting lecture on cetaceans…

Its full title was 'The Evolution of Cetaceans: the Tale of the Whale's Tail from Land to Sea', and it was to be delivered by Garth's marine biologist, a guy by the name of Colin. This chap immediately confessed to being captivated by orcas but was soon telling his assembled audience in the main lounge everything they had ever wanted to know, not about orcas, but about blue whales. It was all pretty interesting stuff.

He kicked off with a discussion of the size of the blue whale – which is nothing short of stupendous. Indeed, how could it not be, thought Brian, when one accepts that it is the largest animal that has ever existed (as far as is known)? Yes, even the biggest dinosaurs could not match the size of this amazing creature – or its weight. For here we are talking about a seagoing behemoth that can measure anything up to one hundred feet in length and weigh in at an incredible 180 tonnes. That's big. In fact, that is unimaginably big for what, after all, is a moving, breathing, thinking, feeling, living organism that has evolved through the process of natural selection. But the tale of its ancestry would have to wait a moment, because Colin was still on the subject of the blue whale's prodigious size – and the equally prodigious size of some of its organs...

The blue whale's tongue, his audience learnt, weighed up to 2.7 tonnes. The creature's heart weighed up to 400 pounds, and if it's a gentleman blue whale then its testes weigh in at 150 pounds apiece – and its penis can have a length of up to ten feet! That last fact grabbed everybody's attention. Brian could sense that he was surrounded by a room full of men attempting to visualise something that size – but failing – and a room full of women attempting to visualise something that size coming towards them – and possibly succeeding. Nobody however dared ask the question that was

62

inevitably on Brian's mind. And that was whether that ten-foot measurement was made when Mr Whale was at rest or when he was suitably excited. It had to be in the excited state, decided Brian. How could it not be? Although, there again, if it was, who had taken the measurement and how the hell had he done it? After all, if attempting to visualise a ten-foot phallus was not that easy, then attempting to visualise a diver with a measuring tape, in intimate contact with an aroused monster in the middle of the ocean, was virtually impossible. Or maybe he just used a theodolite...

Anyway, the lecture moved on – to the blue whale's ancestry, and to the revelation that this enormous creature evolved from a four-legged wolf-sized terrestrial meat-eater! It was quite extraordinary, but it seems that these early carnivores developed a taste for fish and that this pushed them towards a lifestyle that involved their being both on land and in water. Evolution then kicked in – about 50 million years ago – and our early 'wolf' began to evolve to better exploit its watery environment. It started to develop a streamlined body and it slowly adapted its existing physical and sensory equipment for use in the sea. And it appears that it just didn't know when to stop. Which means that what started out as a medium-sized four-legged animal has now become one of the most streamlined creatures of all and, of course, the very largest of all. Unless, of course, one accepts the alternative explanation, involving a fairy with a wand and a pamphlet on so-called intelligent design, who just created the blue whale in its present form out of a lump of ice. And then went on to concoct the orca out of liquorice and the unicorn out of candy.

Unfortunately however, whether one is a disciple of the rational or a bigoted asinine nutter, the fact remains that the blue whale's proportions have not protected it against its much smaller but much more vicious nemesis: us. Yes, here was Brian trying to be upbeat, but Colin the whale man had now launched into that part of his presentation that concerned the hunting of blue whales and the impact this has had on their numbers. Accurate figures, he explained, are difficult to establish, but there is little doubt that before we arrived with the sort of armoury that could overcome the blue whale's speed and power, these creatures were remarkably abundant. There were probably over 250,000 of them in the Antarctic alone. Whereas now... well a 2002 report estimated that there were just 5,000 to 12,000 blue whales in the whole of the world. And even if there are now more than that optimistic 12,000 figure, today's community of blue whales can represent no more than a fragment of their original pre-hunting, pre-exploitation numbers.

Oh dear. Brian needed this presentation to end. Then he needed an immediate distraction. Fortunately, both needs were met. First Colin wrapped up his lecture – with information that of the three blue whale sub-species that are found worldwide, the one that would be encountered in this South Pacific Ocean is the *Balaenoptera musculus brevicauda* sub-species, otherwise known as the *pygmy* blue whale (!) – and then there was a snorkel safety briefing...

Neither Brian nor Sandra were really aficionados of safety briefings, but as they both intended to snorkel on this trip, they had to attend it. Indeed, they wouldn't be issued with any snorkelling kit unless they did. So, with a sizeable complement of other passengers, they remained in their seats and awaited whatever guidance was thought necessary to prevent their coming to grief whilst goggled and flippered. It soon arrived – in the form of a series of dos and don'ts (but mostly don'ts) – delivered by one of the scarier (and sizeable) members of Garth's little team of helpers. This was Ingrid, and Ingrid was a naturalist, a Zodiac driver and the 'snorkel master' (probably, thought Brian, because a 'snorkel mistress' would have conjured up in the minds of most middle-aged men, too many images of an appropriately accessorised dominatrix – probably in a rubber wetsuit). Anyway, what she told her pupils didn't fill Brian with the feeling that snorkelling under her watch would be a very relaxing or very liberating experience. There was even a requirement always to have at your side a 'snorkel buddy', presumably in order to ensure that you and your buddy both felt adequately restrained and adequately pissed off that you couldn't be trusted, even after a lifetime of snorkelling, to look after yourself. 'Elf and safety gone mad,' Brian moaned to his wife. And for once she agreed, and then added that she had no idea how they had both survived snorkelling in the deep waters of the Galápagos only twelve months before – without a single buddy and with only their common sense to rely on.

She didn't stop there. She made some quite

derogatory remarks when, after the catalogue of commands had been delivered in its entirety and before any snorkelling kit had been handed out, a waiver form was produced. This had to be signed by all those wishing to snorkel, and essentially indemnified the tour organisers against the consequences of all sorts of watery mishaps, whether those suffering from these mishaps had a buddy in attendance or not. So, not content with the imposition of some onerous health and safety, the operators had also engaged the services of the legal profession. It was enough, pronounced Sandra, to drive one to drink. Which is the excuse she and her husband used to have a pre-lunch snifter in the bar and slightly more wine than normal during lunch. After which it was definitely time for a short episode of rest back in their cabin before they readied themselves for their next dose of didactic prose. This would again be delivered in the main lounge and it would take the form of a lecture on New Caledonia, a sliver of which would be the ship's destination for the morrow.

Both Brian and Sandra were keen not to miss this. After all, in common with most other Britons, they knew as much about New Caledonia as they did about pneumococcal infections. And furthermore it held out the prospect of being far more interesting than pneumococcal infections. So, when the lecture began, they were all ears, and it began with some basic information about the genesis and the current form of this little known territory.

This took the presenter (an outdoor sort from Australia by the name of Barry) back to a time 140 million years ago. This was when a chunk of land set off eastwards from the supercontinent of Gondwanaland (in fact, from the bit of it that is now the eastern part of Barry's home) and then spent the next 60 million years getting a divorce, to arrive at what is the present day New Caledonia and the present day New Zealand. This, in Brian's mind, meant two things. The first was that as a result of this continental parentage, New Caledonia, unlike lots of other ocean islands, was not the result of volcanic activity, and the second was that the 'New' in both New Caledonia and New Zealand could now be construed as 'only 80 million years old'!

This instant conclusion was soon overturned by further information, and this wasn't just that the 'New' in the divorcees' names was, in fact, not derived from their ancient split. No, it was the revelation that New Caledonia is made up of a number of different elements and that it is only 'Grande Terre' (which is the thin, sausage-shape island that constitutes most of NC's landmass) that is a piece of old Gondwanaland. Its other bits, such as the smaller Loyalty Islands and the even smaller Isle of Pines, did originate from volcanic activity, and are coral islands, created after the old volcanoes sank and the coral reefs rose around them. This was of particular interest to Brian, as it was the Isle of Pines that he would be visiting tomorrow, and he always liked to know whether he was standing on the remains of a supercontinent or on a sunken volcano. Obviously.

Well, Barry's discourse now focused on Grand Terre and the fact that *its* status as a remnant of Gondwanaland, isolated from the rest of the world for all those millions of years, made it a very special place. So it wasn't just a land of tropical forests and savannah, as one might expect, but it was also the place that could claim to have the richest biodiversity in the world (if measured on a 'per square kilometre' basis). It was and still is a real treasure house.

Yes, even though it has been heavily abused by man in the last couple of centuries (so that, for example, only 20% of its indigenous forests now survive) Grand Terre's botany includes not only many endemic species but also entire genera and even families that are unique to the island and are found nowhere else on Earth. As an illustration of this, Barry pointed out that it is blessed with more tropical gymnosperms (basically conifers) than any similar place on the planet, and that of its forty-four indigenous species of gymnosperms, forty-three are endemic and one of these endemics is the only parasitic gymnosperm in the world. It apparently lacks any roots and therefore has to attach itself to the roots of another (endemic) conifer to make a living. Which fact might not set the blood rushing through too many people's veins, but which for Brian was no less than a fascinating revelation. As were the references to some of New Caledonia's fauna.

What stuck in his mind after the presentation were three in particular. The first was a reference to the New Caledonian crow, whose claim to fame is an ability to make tools which rivals that of primates. Indeed it produces tools which are more complex than those produced by any animal other than us. Then there is the endemic kagu, a flightless but agile bird that uses its wings to climb onto branches and occasionally to glide. And last but in no way least, the Ducula goliath, otherwise known as the giant imperial pigeon, and so giant that it is the largest extant pigeon in the world. Whether it knew that it shared New Caledonia with the world's largest gecko species and the world's largest skink species was not covered in the presentation.

Anyway, as touched on already (through that mention of just 20% of NC's indigenous forests remaining), remote treasure houses do not remain remote indefinitely, and sooner or later mankind comes along to... well, to plunder them. And so it was with New Caledonia.

Captain Cook was the first European to set eyes on the place (in 1774) and he was also responsible for giving it its name, having decided that where he landed reminded him of Scotland – or 'Caledonia' (presumably because of its scenery and not because of the presence of biting midges). It then wasn't long before the French were sniffing around, and in due course the British were back and setting up a base to extract whale oil. That was then overtaken by a rush to set up a sandalwood trade – and so began the degradation of not just Grande Terre but also of the Loyalty Islands and the Isle of Pines. Simultaneously, there was an influx of both French and English missionaries, who did nothing to halt the degradation of the environment but who did seek to replace the locals' interest in cannibalism with other pursuits. In the case of the English missionaries, this was with cricket – which is still popular in New Caledonia to this day.

This is where, as Barry explained, things took a turn for the French. Yes, in the 1850s, France was apparently looking for a strategic military location in the Pacific and, more urgently, for a place where it could set up a new penal colony. It seems that, because of the climate, the prisoners in its existing overseas penal colony in French Guiana were suffering from a very high mortality rate. Which, thought Brian, would actually have obviated the need for a new penal colony – as the Guianan one quickly ran out of inmates... However, that clearly hadn't occurred to anyone, and in 1853, France annexed New Caledonia. And Britain did nothing! Heck, not only had we clocked it first, set up business there first and given assorted bits of it English names, but we had even established the sport of cricket there. This was unbelievable, and it certainly didn't go down well in Australia, a country that now found itself with a French presence near one of its principal trade routes and a new nearby penal colony, just after it had managed to abolish convict transportation to its own shores. Barry didn't really explain how this capitulation by Britain had come about, but Brian could only assume that the French announced their annexation on August 12th, a date on which a large proportion of our British Establishment would have been otherwise engaged in dispatching a large proportion of our British wildlife.

Anyway, this was a great shame – especially for the 'Kanaks', the indigenous people of New Caledonia who have yet to feature in its story (even though they had acted as responsible custodians of this wonderful part of the world for centuries). The sandalwood business had already begun to screw up their lives, but as the French settlement process gathered steam, worse was to come. First of all, 'blackbirding' was established, which was the euphemism for enslaving anybody who was black and forcing them to work on the sugar plantations in Fiji and Queensland. Then prisoners released from the penal colony, who were bound to remain in New Caledonia, along with willing settlers from France, began to pursue stuff like cattle farming, which, in contrast to the respect for the environment inherent in Kanak ways, showed only disrespect, both for the environment – and for the Kanaks. Those who weren't killed off by European diseases were put outside the law and became seriously second-class citizens, unconsidered natives who were forced to live in and to stay in designated reservations in Grand Terre's highlands. It is reckoned that their numbers sank from 60,000 in 1878 to just 27,000 in 1921. And certainly their hearts must have sunk when they witnessed the impact on their land of the new nickel industry which kicked off in 1864.

New Caledonia has 25% of the world's nickel supply. This is very good news if one is a worker in the New Caledonian nickel industry and probably even better news if one is a shareholder in this industry. However, it is not such good news for the environment which gets seriously scarred by the mining activity and poisoned by its runoff. Neither is it good news if one is a Kanak. Because as well as one's traditional home being buggered up, one is obliged to accept being made a minority in one's traditional home by the arrival of more and more immigrants to service the nickel industry – on top of your being regarded as little more than a local inconvenience. France, it can be said with certainty, did not cover itself with glory in its treatment or its exploitation of New Caledonia.

Fortunately, with some nudging from the United Nations, things are gradually getting better. France, some time ago, made New Caledonia an overseas territory, with much enhanced rights for all its citizens, and it has at least abandoned its long-standing *indigénat* system, under which it decided every ten years up until WWII that the Kanaks hadn't 'reached sufficient moral and intellectual standards to run their own affairs'. Indeed, in 1987, they held an independence referendum. However, as Barry explained, this followed an extended period of abuse of the Kanaks and a great deal of violence between pro-independence and loyalist supporters, and it was boycotted by the majority of Kanaks. Consequently it was won hands down by the 'outsiders', the native-born French settlers and the more recently arrived French.

This was turning into quite a history lesson, thought Brian, but it was nearing its conclusion. It had to be. It was nearly time for afternoon tea. And indeed when the conclusion did come, it was quite encouraging. Because it seems that the UN nudging has now turned into a really heavy lean on France, in that the French are committed to holding another referendum in 2018. Furthermore, because of the changing demographics in New Caledonia and the rules surrounding the eligibility to vote in this referendum, it is highly likely that the pro-independence guys will win. Of course, if they do, it won't mean that everything will come right overnight, and it may well lead to an almighty mess. Especially in the short term. But right now, there exists a huge income inequality in New Caledonia, and although, with the help of the nickel industry, this territory has the highest GDP per capita in the South Pacific (even higher than that of New Zealand), the Kanaks see little benefit from this economic supremacy. Only with independence, thought Brian, is that situation likely to change – in their favour.

So… an optimistic ending for a pretty disheartening tale. But not optimistic enough for Brian. There might be some sort of salvation for the Kanaks and for their home, but in his mind this hardly made up for what had happened in the past and what is still likely to happen in the future. Accordingly, when he'd returned to his cabin with Sandra, Brian was soon feeling doleful once again. Albeit he couldn't quite make up his mind about what to be doleful…

On the one hand there was huge scope to feel miserable about what we, as the modern manifestation of our species, inflict on this planet – as so eloquently illustrated by our trampling over the settled and sustainable situation we found in New Caledonia. However, this was all a bit old hat, and even with Brian's attempt to update it by considering the silliness of one of the supposedly most intelligent men on the planet, it was still old hat. (This, by the way, is a reference to Professor Hawking's belief that for mankind to secure its future, having almost completely fucked up this world, it will need to colonise another world. This is an idea that not only fails to recognise that we cannot exist without other species but one that ignores the fact that without a shadow of doubt we will fuck up anywhere else we find. Probably a great deal faster than we've fucked up the Earth.)

Or, on the other hand… Brian could depress himself with the thought that what the Europeans did to New Caledonia is currently being mirrored by what is now being done to them. OK, today's Europeans weren't being killed or enslaved, but their home countries were more and more being regarded as 'areas of economic opportunity' rather than places that were formed and shaped by their ancestors and places that consequently furnished these current-day Europeans with a sense of security and more importantly with a sense of their unique identity. Citizenship was being reduced from a birthright to an entitlement – for all-comers. And the result in Britain, France, Germany and many other European countries would very likely be recognised by the majority of Kanaks.

Well, in the end, Brian employed both the old hat and the 'newer hat' broodings to achieve an adequate dose of depression, after which he quickly applied himself to the penning of a couple more limericks. In this way he was in sufficiently sociable form to escort Sandra to a rather missable briefing in the main lounge and to the dinner thereafter. This was again shared with Thor and Lise and Paul and Lydia, all of whom were on particularly good form. Thor expounded his theories on the superiority of internal combustion engine technology over that which facilitates social media, Lise put in a similar case for weaving technology, and then Lydia questioned the merits of any technology other than that which has provided us with drinking water, hot showers and flushing loos. Paul then furnished the group with a sort of non sequitur by suggesting that Mr Putin might be the product of some secret technology gone wrong. And it was after this that Sandra weighed in with a genuine non sequitur, which was to muse on how that parasitic conifer mentioned in the earlier New Caledonian lecture could possibly have come about. Brian's crass answer that this was as a result of its reading too many Labour Party manifestos was not received well – at least by Sandra – but it didn't completely puncture the mood of the meal. Nor did it stop him assaulting Sandra with his two new limericks when they were finally back in their cabin.

The first was:

There was a young woman, Miss Worth
Who loved *saucisson, veau* and rare *boeuf*
In fact, one could say
She loved all things *français*
And that didn't exclude *soixante-neuf*

And the second was:

There was a young lady from Pinner
Whose sex life was like a large dinner
And that is to say
That once every day
She'd like to get quite a lot in 'er

Sandra reacted rather predictably. Her response involved a reference to misogyny and a recommendation that her husband divulge none of these poetic jewels to the rest of the world.

Brian came back with the observation that he hadn't intended to be misogynistic but that he had attempted to be a little or even a lot cruder in his writing, and that he would work on this over the coming few days. In fact, when the exchange was over, he now had something to aim for: a level of crudeness that could match that employed in Sandra's response to this observation. Albeit not necessarily involving the same level of vitriol…

7.

Sandra was much more agreeable in the morning. In fact she was quite cheery when she opened the morning's proceedings, which she did by reminding her husband that they had both somehow missed the crossing of the tropic of Capricorn the previous evening. In response, Brian put forward the explanation that it hadn't been illuminated and therefore it would have been very difficult to spot. Furthermore, as it apparently moves northwards every year by about fifteen metres, it must, he suggested, make any sort of illumination or signposting very difficult indeed…

With Sandra's cheeriness level somewhat reduced, breakfast was dealt with rather expeditiously, and it wasn't long before Brian and Sandra were standing in a queue, suitably life-jacketed and awaiting their turn in a Zodiac. It was still quite early, but the plan was to decant all the ship's passengers onto the Île des Pins (the Frenchified Isle of Pines) as soon as possible to allow them to enjoy both a little bit of exploring and a little bit of snorkelling. And the plan worked very well, helped to no small degree by an extremely calm sea and a conveniently placed and well maintained jetty. This was not to be a repeat of the commando landing on Norfolk

Island. Instead, it was to be a doddle, or as the French administrators of Île des Pins would say, *un morceau de pisse.*

And so it was. Hell, there was even a welcoming committee. This consisted of a group of colourfully dressed lady Kanaks manning a canvas-covered stall and a small troupe of lady and gentlemen Kanaks who were all busy dancing. The stall was loaded with a selection of bananas, handmade flower necklaces and coconut drinks (still in their coconuts). And the troupe was loaded with bushels of dried grass. For the male dancers these bushels had been fashioned into a decoration for their calves, waists and heads, and for both gender of dancers more of them had then been recruited to the cause of 'grassy swatters'. The men were also loaded with white paint – on their bare torsos and on their faces. The overall effect was remarkable and like nothing Brian had ever experienced in Calais.

Now, he had made this comparison in his mind, because Île des Pins is part of New Caledonia, and New Caledonia, as already discussed, is a French overseas territory. In fact, it has a special status as an overseas territory which reflects the gradual transfer of power from the French state to New Caledonia itself, and this special status means that its citizens, for the time being at least, still retain French citizenship and French voting rights (as well as enjoying a new New Caledonian citizenship). So... this arrival onto Île des Pins was tantamount to an arrival in France itself, other than it was definitely more humid and, of course, coconut drinks and dancing natives decorated with straw and paint barely featured at any of the French ferry ports that Brian had used in the past.

Anyway, whatever its political status, Île des Pins was quite a place. Its nickname, Brian had discovered, was *l'île la plus proche du paradis* (the closest island to paradise) and he had already clocked from the ship that it was a pretty impressive-looking spot. It was similar in size to somewhere like Guernsey, but it had a population of just 2,000 – mostly Kanaks – and it seemed to have retained much of its original vegetation. This was possibly because ship masts made out of *Araurcaria columnaris* would be even worse than those made out of Norfolk Island pines. In fact, it wouldn't take a mast maker to realise that this island's variety of pines, after which it is named and which still grow in profusion, wouldn't make even a decent flagpole for a ship's pennant. They look more like large, green pipe cleaners than they do trees, and they seem to major on the 'not quite upright and a bit wobbly-looking'. So whilst definitely attractive, they are not the sort of plants that would ever have set Captain Cook's heart racing and instead might even have put a smile on his face. They really are more tropical-utopian than they are utilitarian, and consequently they have largely been left alone.

Well, now it was time to explore the closest island to paradise, and after having supped some coconut milk and decorated their hats with those necklaces of flowers, that's exactly what Brian and Sandra did. There were options. And they had opted for a walk through a forested area just beyond the jetty in the company of Owen (the tour's resident ornithologist and hobbit) and a dozen or so other passengers. Yes, this was the birding group, and their intention was to see... birds. Unfortunately, nobody had given prior notice to Île des Pins' birds, and they essentially failed to turn up. It was just too late in the day, and the only avian interruption to the meander through the forest was a New Caledonian friarbird (a relative of the 'noisy friarbird' [really] found in New Guinea and eastern Australia).

Anyway, it had been an interesting enough walk – through all those pipe cleaners – and there was still coconut milk awaiting for the birders when they returned to the jetty. There were also the remnants of yet another penal colony here, this one built and used to house all those bothersome Kanaks who'd had the temerity to challenge French occupation, along with political deportees from France itself. Yes, during that inglorious period of French absolute domination and repression, Kanak chiefs and other senior figures in their community were exiled to Île des Pins to share their lives with similar non-people from France's revolutionary 'Paris Commune'. Inevitably, some of these unfortunates didn't ever leave Île des Pins, and not far from the remains of the penal colony is the *Cimetière des Déportés,* which in the interests of avoiding condescension will not be translated. Once again, thought Brian, we seemed to excel in identifying adversaries of some sort and then penalising them – sometimes literally – and we still do. It's just mildly good news, he also thought, that we don't still use places close to paradise to do this.

OK, nature and history now dealt with, it was time for a bit of snorkelling. This was to be conducted off a beach just a few hundred yards from the jetty, and it proved popular with quite a few of the ship's passengers. Unfortunately, the sight of one of these passengers emerging from the water with a bloodied foot, just as Brian and Sandra were arriving on the beach, meant that it wouldn't be quite so popular with them. And apparently, the owner of the bloodied foot had even had her snorkelling buddy in attendance…

So Mr and Mrs Wimp forwent a watery immersion and went instead to sit on a log where they made friends with a dog but not with the osprey that was diving for fish in the sea. And then it was time to return to the *Caledonian Sky* before it set sail just after noon for its next destination. Île des Pins had been 'done' – insofar as one can do it in three hours – and Brian had come away with the impression that it was a little more Melanesian than Norfolk Island. At least it still had more than an odd sprinkling of trees, and it had people who danced in grass skirts and it didn't seem to have any cows.

Toby and Gillian – who did have cows – more or less agreed with this assessment of Île des Pins. They were cattle farmers from Yorkshire who had joined Brian and Sandra for lunch – along with another pair by the names of David and Ruth who kept only cocker spaniels. It proved to be a very pleasant lunch, although Brian was not sure that he should have asked David, when Ruth had popped to the loo, whether her not being around caused him to feel ruthless. His reaction appeared to suggest that he either hadn't understood the pun or had heard it ten thousand times before.

Anyway, lunch – and more lunchtime drinking –

eventually came to an end, and it was recuperation time. It had been an early start to the day, Île des Pins' humid climate had been draining – as had the draining of all those glasses over lunch – and it was definitely time to retire to one's cabin. There, if one was Brian, one might then decide, that rather than just lying on a bed, one could indulge in a bit of 'Trump-time'.

Yes, those two news channels on the in-cabin telly that Brian had discovered three days before were *US* news channels and they were essentially devoted to the coverage of Donald Trump's embryonic presidency – and how badly or how well it was going depending on whether it was Reasonable Channel A or Delusional (full of plastic people) Channel B that was providing the analysis.

It was all captivating stuff, not least because Brian had already been enthralled by the fact that somebody like Mr Trump had been elevated to the presidency of the United States and that, now he was there, some people were actually taking him seriously. In Brian's mind – where account had been taken of Brian's current nautical situation – it was a bit like the daftest solution possible to resolving the problem of a poor ship's captain. OK, the passengers and crew of the SS *United States* had been unhappy for some time with how a succession of captains had run the ship. After all, they all seemed not to know how to do this either efficiently or fairly and they didn't seem to have a very clear idea as to where they were taking their vessel. It was in 'drift mode' and there was every possibility that it could drift into real trouble.

Solution? Scrub the idea of recruiting a new, trained captain, and instead have an on-board lottery, and put in charge of the ship whoever wins it. Hey presto, one has one's new skipper, and on this occasion it just so happens to be one of the ship's entertainment contingent. Yes, you've ended up with that middle-aged, bordering-on–the-corpulent, coiffured guy whose job it was to act as the master of ceremonies at the ship's interminable talent contests – and as the ship's principal bingo caller. Oh, and his knowledge of maritime matters was restricted to his remembering that in the event of a ship sinking it was advisable to find oneself a bath cap in order to ensure that one's coiffure was not compromised by the action of seawater on one's bonce.

So now he sits on the bridge – after it had been explained to him where the bridge was – and he doesn't actually steer the ship or look after its affairs, but instead he issues orders. He dreams up commands, and his newly installed crew – consisting mostly of his fellow 'entertainers' and a couple of clerks from the purser's office – are charged with implementing them without question. This strategy has, it must be confessed, proved quite problematical, and this outcome is not unconnected with the nature – and the complete impracticality – of most of his commands. It nearly proved possible to turn the comms room into a recording studio, but they then had to reinstall the comms equipment when it became apparent that the captain couldn't use his Twitter account any more. Other orders didn't even get that far. Hell, nobody could work out how to fit a full-sized golf course on the ship, and gold-plating the ship's engines was a complete non-starter. Then there was his 'Executive Order of the Highest Importance' to build a high-rise on top of the bridge. This, he claimed, would become the most desirable of exclusive condominiums bar none – providing regular access for the condominium occupants to the captain's table and assorted world leaders for a modest annual premium, payable in cash.

Well, there began to be rumbles of discontent. The captain's approval ratings were in freefall. Which is why the captain installed, as his very own special spokesman, a guy who used to be a stoker on the ship and who initially thought that 'disseminate' was something women did after sex – with the help of a douche. He wasn't a great success, partly because he modelled his style – and his haircut – on that guy who used to hold rallies at Nuremberg. And that didn't go down well. Especially when he grew himself that toothbrush moustache…

So his boss was left floundering, as was more than apparent when Brian tuned into Reasonable Channel A. Because here they were showing aerial views of Mr Trump's inauguration and similar views from President Obama's previous inauguration, which clearly showed, just as his spokesman was confidently denying, that fewer people had turned up to see a joke president inaugurated than a real one. Whether Mr Trump believed his own skewed interpretation of the facts, Brian did not know, but that this new president would turn out to be the worst president in the history of the United States was a racing cert. And in the meantime he would provide endless fun to all those who took even a passing interest in world affairs – and endless embarrassment to all those Americans who had more than burger meat between their ears. That said, Brian was not receptive to some of the more outlandish claims made about this dysfunctional commander, not least the one that suggested that he washed his hair in wee wee to retain its golden hue. After all, he reckoned, even a knobhead wouldn't want to smell of urine…

Brian finally turned off the telly. There was only so much humour one could take in one session. And after a slight resting of his eyes, he found himself slipping into that blasted melancholia again, and for reasons that were far from clear, his route into today's black hole was through a door designated 'men only' – and it wasn't the gents. It was a portal into a critique of men as the dominant gender and of all the men who practise this dominance – even if they didn't look like or act like Donald J Trump.

So, as far as Brian was concerned, if one was attempting to decide which gender of the human species was the more destructive, devastating, dangerous and deluded, it would have to be men. Armed with a residue of their cavemen past called testosterone, they now constitute not only the greatest peril to the planet (as apparent on somewhere like New Caledonia) but also the greatest threat to that other gender of our species known as women.

Yes, pondered Brian, if we're cutting down trees, slaughtering sharks or catching defenceless songbirds in lime nets, then the 'we' is almost invariably men. They are the guys who do the actual damage. And they are the guys who start wars, continue wars and restart wars. One only has to turn on the telly and if it's got a bandolier of bullets over its shoulder and an AK-47 in its hands, or if it's firing off hundreds of bullets into thin air (why do they do that?) then it's a pretty good bet that it's a man. Mind, thought Brian, this war stuff wasn't just testosterone in play. It was also: 'well it's a darned sight more fun than getting a nine to five job or having to look after the kids or do the washing-up'. Yes, there was no doubt in his mind. Men, as well as being stupid, were easily addicted. Especially when that addiction allowed them to skip personal hygiene, any sort of chores, any real responsibility, and instead gave them an opportunity to sit in the back of a pickup looking like an extra from *Mad Max*, whilst smoking incessantly – and firing all those rounds into the air to no effect whatsoever.

Of course, considered Brian, there are limits to how many wars the human race can sustain at one time, and most men now have to make do with a football match or a PlayStation rather than an AK-47. Whilst others maintain the existence of religions and thereby help to maintain the dominance of their kind over women.

Yes, it is no coincidence, Brian believed, that all religions are effectively run by men and that all religions are essentially dismissive of women. These poor souls are either second-class nothings or, worse, a source of temptation, put there by God to divert men from their spiritual interaction with their creator. And this wasn't sophistry. All the 'great' religions have had it in for women from their inception and some of them still conduct their affairs as though the subjugation of the fairer sex is their primary objective. And no great surprise. Because it's what men want. It's that testosterone again. It stimulates the desire to dominate. Not just their enemies, but for many men, their female partners whom they see (although they might not recognise this) as a potential threat to their dominance. After all, with all their despicable sexual shenanigans, women can overcome men, and they do – and this earns them a man's disdain and even a man's utmost contempt. And the only way to deal with these hussies is to turn up the burner. More dominance, more disrespect, more abuse – and more of the appalling treatment of that one half of humanity that the men-dominated religions sanction as merely reasonable and proper.

It was indisputable. Men are bad news. Some men are the worst news possible. And they can even be responsible for leading one of their fellow number into another black hole. Shit, thought Brian, he'd better get down to some more limericks just as soon as he could.

This he did, but it meant that he and Sandra missed the afternoon's briefing on what they would be doing tomorrow. Neither of them thought this too important as their itinerary indicated that this would be a visit to another island but not until tomorrow afternoon. So there would be plenty of time to discover whatever they needed to know. Just as there would be no time at all to equip themselves with 'tropical/colourful clothing'! Yes, Sandra had belatedly established that this evening's dinner would be a 'tropical dinner', and one was requested to dress accordingly. Even if one was a reserved dresser whose wardrobe, in the case of Brian, was essentially a study in blues with the occasional black and grey. So, in due course, Sandra appeared for this themed repast in some almost suitable garb, accompanied by her husband who had at least managed to find a red-coloured hanky. He was quite pleased when the event was over and thereafter eschewed the tropical festivities in the Panorama Lounge in favour of a three-limerick recital back in his cabin. Directly after that black hole experience, he had been a very busy boy.

The three odes, delivered one after the other to Sandra, were as follows:

> There was a young man from Dumfries
> Who with bras found them hard to release
> So off they would come
> O'er hips an' o'er bum
> With the help of a handful of grease

And

> There was a young man from Carlisle
> Who hadn't had sex for a while
> So he had to make do
> With an open-toed shoe
> And a remodelled lever arch file

And

> There was a young chappie from Crewe
> Whose 'transactions' with ladies were few

In fact they were none
And all he had done
Was once get a full frontal view

Sandra didn't pass judgement immediately, but when she did it was succinct. It was 'gross, distasteful and even more distasteful in that order'.

Brian smiled. Praise indeed. At this rate he was well on his way to achieving the sort of crude stuff that would make even a sailor blush. Although probably not Mr Trump…

$8.$

Today would see Brian and Sandra visiting not just a new island but a brand new country. Yes, soon after lunch they would be stepping foot on Vanuatu, a country they knew little about, other than that it was essentially a string of volcanic islands supposedly covered in lush forests and originally known as the New Hebrides. That, of course, was that Captain Cook guy again, who in 1774 stumbled across the island chain – and either had never seen the Inner or the Outer Hebrides or was having some sort of joke. No way, thought Brian, could anybody accuse any of the Hebridean islands of being covered in lush forests, and there was a bit of a temperature difference as well.

Anyway, a new country, however inappropriate its original name, was just what Brian needed to stave off another bout of melancholia. Already weakened by his repeated application of limericks, it didn't stand a chance. Or it wouldn't have if he hadn't awoken with another reason to feel depressed already forming in his mind. It was there as he opened his eyes and it was still there after breakfast, and he simply could not ignore it. He therefore made the remarkably stupid decision to eschew the morning's presentation on Vanuatu and work on this latest 'topic of gloom' while Sandra attended the presentation and thereby left him alone to do so. Oh, and the topic had the snappy title of 'the opportunities for wealth creation in different cultures'. He suspected he probably needed professional help, but for now he comforted himself with the thought that he had arrived at this new subject as a result of yesterday's account of how the French had created wealth for themselves at the expense of the original inhabitants of New Caledonia. Or maybe not. Who could tell?

In any event, after a rather tetchy Sandra had left him, he was soon on the job, and to start with he once again considered the exploitation of New Caledonia by the French and by other Europeans, and focused on the fact that many of these exploiters hadn't come halfway around the world to make a living but instead they'd made that long journey to make a killing. It was one of the few ways that people not necessarily born into wealth in the eighteenth and nineteenth centuries could accumulate some serious wealth, especially if they had little regard for any of the damage they might cause and no regard whatsoever for any of the black people they might encounter. Accordingly, many of them made fortunes out of the sandalwood trade, out of nickel mining and, of course, out of 'blackbirding'.

With this 'serious wealth creation' starting point established, Brian then fast-forwarded to the present day to consider how the modern inhabitants of France and all the other old colonial powers now go about building up a big pile of loot. And if one discounts involvement in one of the purely criminal pastimes involving drugs, fraud or banking, say, then it generally involves their using a mix of inventiveness, creativity, risk-taking and sheer hard work – with maybe just a soupçon of sharp practice or rule-bending at the outset. They use the capitalist system and the operation of free markets to build businesses – and wealth – often to the benefit of others and sometimes without doing a great deal of damage. And, of course, it's the same in North America and Australasia. In essence, all those countries that were the source of thoughtless, in-it-for-themselves buccaneers are now those countries that enable any of their citizens who are blessed with both imagination and perseverance to end up with a considerable pile of dosh – largely legitimately.

So far so good. Nothing to get too depressed about there. But it was now time to consider all those countries outside Europe, North America and Australasia where application with dedication is not the route to 'above-average' wealth, but instead if one wants to acquire lots of riches one must first acquire (or retain) political power. Yes, in Brian's mind, most of the world was not fertile ground for entrepreneurial effort of any sort, but instead a barren wasteland where it was recognised that to create one's own luxurious oasis one had first to secure power and then to hold on to that power as if one's life depended on it. Which it quite often did.

This was really depressing. But to ensure that it was overwhelmingly depressing, Brian began to work his way through that sterile wasteland – and he started with Africa. Here was a continent which, with a couple of notable exceptions, was just stuffed with countries where presidential power was often unfettered and where presidential wealth was immense and shared only with a political elite. While the vast majority of their citizens just about survive – or don't even manage that – those at the top travel around in private jets, go shopping in London or Singapore, and are never seen outside their mansions other than in a convoy of armour-plated limousines or behind armour-plated screens at some tacky, stage-managed rally, intended to display to the plebs their bogus popularity and their very genuine power. They are just gangsters, completely corrupt leaders who feed off the natural wealth of their countries – along with a side order of international aid – whilst ensuring that any genuine entrepreneurs, if they've got any sense, will ship themselves off to the US or Europe before you can say 'mine's a Mugabe'.

They won't, of course, head for Russia. Here, Brian knew, was a true kleptocracy, where the serf mentality of a whole nation has been exploited by a bunch of villains masquerading as the country's national leadership, and whole swathes of the country's national wealth has been funnelled into the pockets of the powerful. Yes, mere hundreds of Russia's citizens have accumulated enough wealth to enable them to buy London properties, French vineyards and ghastly superyachts, and have done this not through any sort of honest toil but by being in power or by colluding with and supporting those who themselves are in power. Finding a Russian oligarch who has amassed his wealth through creativity, inventiveness, hard work or imagination is as difficult as finding one who understands the meaning of sophistication. In essence, they are a bunch of guys who realised very early on that in the sort of culture that still smells of tsars and peasants, there was no point in building a new Facebook empire (which they wouldn't have known how to do anyway) but every point in either grabbing political power or in being of assistance to those who had chosen to do this as their post-KGB career move.

India, Brian believed, was different, but not much better. Here, after all, political power was not just a route to wealth but it could also help one avoid the consequences of one's criminal past (and present). Pakistan, on the other hand, majored in the employment of political power, in what is essentially a feudal society, to ensure that those in power retained and increased their super wealth for their own benefit and for the benefit of their extended families. The other 'Stans' seemed to be variants of this model, and then, of course, there was China.

Well, it's probably enough to say that the ruling elite here practise not communism but 'corruptism' – to their enormous economic advantage. Brazil's leaders, as well, seem to have been tempted recently by the power of power to enrich along with Venezuela's dysfunctional rulers, but they are only amateurs compared to their counterparts in the Gulf. Here, the game isn't to secure power to become filthy rich but more to retain power to remain filthy rich. Nowhere is this more evident, Brian believed, than in Saudi Arabia, a country that is more a family possession than it is a true nation state. And the family isn't about to give up its possession – or its fabulous wealth – because it certainly isn't about to give up its power. Indeed, political power throughout the Gulf tends to shift about as much as attitudes to female emancipation do – which is at an imperceptible rate or not at all. It will therefore be an absolute age before the Saudi family's grip on power slips and the Frobishers start to accumulate a pile of loot in Frobisher Arabia…

So, Brian was left with the unavoidable conclusion that in this modern, post-colonial world, not only have we a dysfunctional dominant species but this same species, in most of the world, lives within dysfunctional societies. The planet is burdened with cultures that offer 'extreme financial benefit', not through the use of one's brain or through inventiveness and application, but through the grasping of power and then the exercise of this power primarily or solely for the purpose of personal enrichment. It was enough to make an optimist morose. Which meant it was enough to make Brian glum beyond words.

He therefore decided that he'd better stop all this nonsense now, and get on with some limerick writing – before Sandra returned from her lecture. And this is what he did, so that when Sandra arrived back in the cabin he felt only a very light shade of blue. He was even able to smile as she walked through the door.

'How did it go?' he enquired. 'Anything interesting?'

'Well and yes,' responded Sandra precisely, 'You should have been there.'

'Yeah, well…'

'Yes, you should have been there.'

Brian adopted his sheepish look and ventured a plaintive plea.

'I don't suppose you'd like to…'

'…give you a precis?' finished Sandra.

'Well, if it was interesting…'

Sandra rolled her eyes, but then she sat down on one of the cabin's chairs and appeared to be collecting her thoughts. Then she began to deliver her didactic distillation.

'Right. First Vanuatu. In a nutshell: eighty-three volcanic islands stretching in a long chain between the tropic of Capricorn and the equator, with a total land area of about 12,000 square kilometres. It sits on the edge of the Pacific tectonic plate which unsurprisingly means that it suffers from frequent earthquakes and volcanic eruptions. In fact, I think Bob – the guy who gave the lecture – said that if you factor in all the cyclones Vanuatu suffers, it's one of the most 'lively' places to live anywhere on Earth.'

'I can imagine.'

'OK. Errh, do you want to know the bad stuff?'

'You mean the environmental stuff?'

'Yep.'

'Well…'

'It's only as you'd expect. You know, lots of introduced invasive species buggering up the flora 'n' fauna, lots of illegal logging, lots of problems with fresh water supplies – and habitats – lots of Japanese and Korean fishing boats plundering their fish stocks, and the international tropical-fish trade depleting the stock of the smaller chaps. I mean, you must remember that dreadful *Finding Nemo* film and how every kid suddenly wanted a clownfish. Well, Vanuatu was where they came from – and where they are still coming from. The trade in these chaps is screwing up things a treat.'

Brian was beginning to feel… depressed. He wished he hadn't asked. But Sandra was now moving on from nature to nationhood – and how Captain Cook's New Hebrides came to be the independent nation of Vanuatu. Basically, she explained, it all started much as it had in New Caledonia. The Brits and French arrived and made the most of their new find with lots of sandalwood activity and lots of blackbirding activity, and when the settler numbers began to increase, they showed little if any regard for the locals (and certainly none for those of them who had dined on some of the early missionaries). However, having left any hint of an *entente cordiale* back in Europe, the French and Brits were beginning to be almost as horrible to each other as they were to the locals. Brawls and fights were becoming common and it looked as though things could get really out of hand. So in 1906 the almost impossible happened. Because the British and French governments got together and created the 'Anglo-French Condominium of the New Hebrides'.

What this meant was that the British and French nationals were granted equal rights – and the locals none – and the territory was lumbered with British and French courts to sort out disputes between their own nationals, a joint court to sort out disputes between the British and the French and all the other Europeans and the locals – and, of course, another one for sorting out problems between the unfortunate locals themselves (but unsurprisingly not presided over by any of the locals). Then there were two police forces, two education systems, two prison systems, two currencies and even two sets of rules for the road. Although it was unclear from the morning's presentation whether this meant that the French drove on the right and the Brits on the left.

Another term for this condominium was a joke, and it became an ever more unsustainable joke after the Second World War. Land ownership – and exploitation – became a real issue by the mid-sixties, and eventually and very painfully this led to the dissolution of the biggest duplication joke in history in 1980 and the granting of independence to the new nation of Vanuatu on 30th July of that year.

This is where the story got particularly interesting for Brian. Because, despite the lifting of that double colonial yoke, things didn't turn out as well as was hoped. That is to say that the early days of independence were characterised by political crimes, nepotism, police mutinies and the odd riot. Things did eventually calm down but (and this was what Brian found really intriguing), as recently as 2015, fourteen of the country's fifty-two MPs, including the deputy PM, were found guilty of corruption and taking bribes, and were thrown into jail for up to four years. And if that wasn't a vindication of Brian's earlier castigation of the majority of the world's leaders and politicians then he was a clownfish. And he wasn't. So, he decided, it must be. Although there again, fair dos for Vanuatu in that they did actually identify all those corrupt buggers and then lock them all up. If only, thought Brian, that could happen in the rest of the world…

'I suppose I should give you a quick rundown on Tanna.'

This was Sandra, committing herself to a further precis, this time of what she had learnt this morning about the island they would be visiting soon after lunch.

She continued.

'Right. It's at the southern tip of the Vanuatu chain. It's about twenty-five miles by twelve miles. It was given its name by Captain Cook (!) – probably from the local name for earth, which is 'tana'. It's populated almost entirely by Melanesians and they largely follow a much more traditional lifestyle than in the rest of Vanuatu. But what's really interesting about Tanna is that it is essentially the world capital of cargo cults…'

'Ah, yes. I've heard about them.'

'Yes, well Bob explained them in some detail, and how they've been observed in other places like Fiji and New Guinea when a very traditional culture makes first contact with a technologically advanced one and…'

'…the traditional culture tries to make sense of the experience,' finished Brian.

'Yes,' confirmed Sandra. 'Something like that. And in the case of Tanna, it started in the thirties with some mysterious guy called John Frum, but then really took off after World War II. You see, the locals had observed stuff being airdropped to the American troops during the war – or landed on airstrips – and what they made of this was… well, that all this stuff that they'd never seen before, like canned foods and manufactured clothes, must have been created by spiritual means, and that somehow these strange foreigners had gained control of the process. And what's more that at some time in the future their ancestors or maybe it was their deities – I'm a little vague on that – would wrest back control and then supply all these goodies to…'

'… all the dedicated members of the cult.'

'Spot on,' confirmed Sandra. 'But the cult members had to participate in various ritualistic acts. And that's what they did after the war – building military-like airstrips in the jungle, building life-sized replicas of aeroplanes out of straw, and even staging military-like drills with sticks for guns and with military style insignia painted on their bodies. Oh, and they were building radios out of coconuts and straw and headphones out of wood…'

'It's all a bit sad, isn't it?'

'Yes, it is. Particularly when you learn that the cults were generally created by some of the 'big men' in society and… well, they might not have been entirely sincere. They might have been making the most of some very gullible people.'

'What's new?'

'Yes. Well, anyway, the John Frum cult is still going. And there's another one called the Tom Navy cult. And then there's the Prince Philip Movement. And as far as I can remember this Prince Phil thing stemmed from a legend involving some son of a mountain spirit who cleared off to a distant land, from where he would return when he'd married a powerful woman. And I think he might be related to John Frum and he's definitely regarded as a divine being – and not as a grumpy old so and so…'

'Amazing. And this is where we're going after lunch?'

'It is. But I don't think you need worry. Nobody on Tanna is going to mistake you for a divine being.'

And with that reassurance delivered, Sandra then suggested to her husband that he get himself ready for an early lunch. The sooner they ate, she explained, the sooner they would be able to get to the top deck, and there observe the ship's approach to Cargo Cult Central. This, she further explained, promised to be spectacular – because Cargo Cult Central had, towering above it, a very active volcano…

And there it was, beyond a ridge of lush vegetation: the towering Mount Yasur volcano, with above it an enormous plume of ash and smoke. It was an intoxicating sight and at the same time a rather sobering sight, and sobering because for quite a number of the ship's complement the real purpose of the visit to Tanna was to inspect this volcano at close range. They would be driving to its crater to observe that plume at *unnervingly* close range. Oh, and both Brian and Sandra, the previous evening, had casually signed up for this volcano trek.

Brian was still questioning the wisdom of this decision when his Zodiac was approaching a charcoal-coloured Tanna beach, but then he began to question the wisdom of attempting to land on this beach. He'd known it would be a wet landing in the surf, but he hadn't been pre-warned that the surf would be quite so vigorous and that the steep shelving of the beach made any landings here something of a challenge. Furthermore there were scores and scores of the locals on the beach, all no doubt anticipating how waves of oldies were going to cope with waves of water as they attempted to disembark each Zodiac and make it to shore.

However, it wasn't too bad. Garth's team had stationed themselves in the water and made each Zodiac emptying almost easily manageable. Then the assembled Tannans were quick to offer their smiles and more coconut refreshments as the oldies discarded their lifejackets – before leading them to a line of trucks…

There didn't seem to be a village near the beach, but just a track leading away from it, at the bottom of which were assembled seven not-entirely-in-showroom-condition pickups. No matter. It soon became apparent that to negotiate that track – as it rose up and up and up – one definitely needed 4x4 pickups and, as long as they worked, their condition was entirely irrelevant. Nothing else would have managed it. That said, what was not quite so apparent at the outset was that one really needed something padded to sit on to negotiate the track in any degree of comfort. But all there was in the back of each pickup were planks…

Now, it should be noted that the drive to the top of the volcano was scheduled to take almost an hour (in fact, it took more than an hour) and the track available for this drive was appalling. It was unsurfaced and uncompromising in its impact on rigid pickup suspensions. This meant – for Brian at least – that when his own pickup moved off with, aboard it, seven other victims, including Sandra, his first thought was that he might experience some discomfort. Within just two minutes he then thought he might experience some serious discomfort, and this was confirmed just two minutes later. Then discomfort morphed into an achy sort of pain – in his left buttock – before he shifted his buttocks when the pain then developed in his right buttock. Soon after this, it was all about double buttock pain, relieved only by repeated twinges in his back. The pickup was conspiring with the track to provide frequent jolts to its passengers, and if one was bent over slightly to avoid one's head making contact with the pickup's metal tarpaulin frame above said head, one was not in the optimum position to deal with these jolts.

Never mind. Because one could always distract oneself from this purgatory by catching glimpses of the jungle-like vegetation on either side of the track and one could also snatch the occasional view of the volcano which seemed to be no closer than it was when one last saw it or when one last saw it before that. This drive was simply never going to end. Indeed, even when the jungle was abandoned in favour of a moonlike landscape, created no doubt by the volcano's exhalations, its crater seemed as far away as ever. Until it wasn't. Yes, quite suddenly, just after Brian's pickup had run the gauntlet of a number of steaming fissures to the side of the track, the crater emerged into view. And Brian realised why that investment in more than an hour's worth of painful confinement in the back of a pickup had been worth it after all.

This was Brian and Sandra's fourth experience of a volcano but easily their most dramatic. Directly above where the pickup had dropped them was the plume of 'stuff' that they'd seen from the ship, but now so close that it was depositing a continuous rain of ash onto their heads. It was also a plume that was being continually charged with more 'stuff' by a series of ominous volcano-scale belches. For half a minute or so there would be a distinct period of quiescence and this would then end with a burst of steam and ash, accompanied at its conclusion with a fountain of 'bigger bits', rocks and assorted gobbets of lava which would happily hurtle skywards.

This was a truly impressive display, not least because the *Caledonian Sky's* shipmates had been allowed to climb up to a point that was very close to the crater rim. It transpired that this was because the volcano's activity was merely at level two – where level one is just ticking over and level five is 'emigrate from Tanna immediately'. Whether this was an accurate or reliable measure, Brian could not tell. But what he did know was that if this volcano had this level of activity in England, viewing would require a mandatory health and safety briefing before one was then allowed to within just two miles of its crater.

It didn't smell much. That was the initial topic of conversation as Brian's pickup began its downward journey and another period of acute discomfort, one now made worse by a combination of gritty volcano ash and perspiration about one's body. Yes, the volcano had barely any discernible sulphur smell despite its constant stream of ashy belches. And this was very peculiar. As was the small herd of cows which was making its way across the barren ash-field near the peak of the volcano. The cows had no cowman with them and Brian wondered whether they were escapees from Norfolk Island, following in the traditions of Melanesian and Polynesian navigators as they sought out a new place to live.

Interestingly, this urge to explore, demonstrated by South Pacific travellers in the past, was revisited during dinner. Everybody had returned to the ship, had treated themselves to an extended and much-needed shower, and having endured another briefing by Garth, they were now enjoying a much-needed meal. And amongst them, in the Bridge Deck restaurant were the gang of six: Brian, Sandra, Thor, Lise, Paul and Lydia. And it was Thor who advised his fellow table companions that those South Pacific sailors, in their fragile wooden longboats, employed a very neat and very effective method of navigation. This involved their jumping out of their boats and then feeling the current against their testicles, in order to decide which way to go. Paul then confessed that he'd tried something similar in Bridlington – to establish the direction of the tide – and had got into all sorts of trouble. At which point Brian lowered the tone of the conversation even more by claiming that he had tried the Paul trick, but that because of the size of his adjacent breakwater his testicles had not been able to discern any movement in the water whatsoever…

In most marriages that would have constituted quite enough vulgarity for the day. However there were still those earlier composed limericks to deal with. So, as soon as Brian and Sandra were back in their cabin, their marriage was further embellished with a final slug of crudity. It was in the form of two doses and these two doses were as follows:

There was a nude man called Al Core
Who plugged in a circular saw
He put it to use
With his manhood still loose
And now Al's not a man any more

And

There was a young chappie called Ken
Whose penis was two foot and ten
For most of the time
He controlled it just fine
But it did trip him up now and then

Sandra handed down her judgement. It was that whilst she was not completely anti-male genitalia per se, she did think that they had been given rather too much exposure this evening, and there was a limit to just how much male genitalia one could handle at one time. In fact, she added, it was actually a very low limit, and tonight it had been comfortably exceeded. One could even say, she suggested, by about two foot and four.

And she wondered why her husband got depressed…

9.

When Brian awoke in the morning, Sandra was already up and was standing at the cabin window. She turned to look at her husband and greeted him with some information.

'Good morning,' she announced, 'you should get up and look at this. We're in Havannah harbour.'

'Did you say Havana harbour?' managed Brian.

'No. I said good morning…'

'Oh yes, good morning.'

'…and I said *Havannah* harbour, as in a fabulous natural harbour off Efate, which, of course, has nothing to do with the capital of Cuba…'

'You've lost me.'

'God. Don't you remember anything from yesterday's briefing?'

'Not a lot.'

Sandra harrumphed and then attempted to educate her husband.

'Right. We've sailed overnight to Efate. It's the most populous island in Vanuatu and the island that hosts the country's capital, Port Vila.'

'Oh yes, I remember. It's the place that Captain Cook named Sandwich Island – after the Earl of Sandwich. I mean, blimey, that chap never missed an opportunity to butter up his friends, did he?'

'Yes. Well, you might also remember that we are not planning to visit Efate, but instead we've parked in Havannah harbour – which, as you might or might not remember, is the natural harbour formed by Efate and two small islands off its coast called Lelepa and Moso. And the reason we're parked here is that we'll be visiting both these islands – starting with Lelepa this morning.'

Brian's countenance changed – for the worse. He had at last remembered a little more than how Captain Cook sought to ingratiate himself to people, and it was the rather more pertinent fact that this first visit of the day would be to inspect some… cave paintings. As he then hauled himself out of bed – to inspect the panorama of Havannah harbour – his countenance deteriorated further. And this was because he had just realised that his back had suffered some serious harm from that pickup-up-a-volcano trip of the previous day. It had hardly bothered him after the event, but now it was making itself known in no uncertain terms. It was awful.

He was therefore presented with a dilemma. On the one hand he had the once-in-a-lifetime opportunity to visit a very special cave, a large decorated cavern that was part of a UNESCO World Heritage site called Chief Roi Mata's Domain (which encompassed a chunk of Efate, Lelepa and another island called Eretoka – which was where the thirteenth-century Melanesian Chief Roi was buried along with twenty-five of his retinue). Or, on the other hand, he could duck out of this visit and not only rest his damaged back but also avoid what were, in his experience, the two guaranteed features of any visit to a cave to inspect its cave paintings. These were a) an awkward ascent to the cave in humid or hot conditions and b) a display of images on the cave walls that were a mix of the indistinct, the disappointing, the childish and the plain tedious.

Well, it took him less time to resolve the dilemma than it took Sandra to decide to go on her own. She had her own reservations about caves and indeed enclosed spaces of any sort whatsoever, but she didn't have a bad back and neither did she have Brian's tendency to so readily... back out or... cave in.

Accordingly, three hours later, Brian was able to report to Sandra that he had enjoyed an extended session of limerick writing – while he rested his back – and Sandra was able to report to Brian that the cave visit had been relatively rewarding, albeit there was an unwelcome climb to its entrance. As regards the paintings themselves... well, there were some that were no more than spots and handprints and these were apparently up to 3,000 years old. Then there were others that were essentially line drawings of things like fish, birds and triangles, and whilst some of these were possibly centuries old as well, most were only 300 years old. So... although Sandra was attempting to sound marginally enthusiastic, Brian formed his own second-hand impression of what he had missed. It was an impression that would not be changing his previous opinion of the merits or otherwise of visiting caves for the express purpose of viewing cave paintings. He was reassured that he had chosen wisely and what's more, he now had a whole fistful of limericks. As Sandra would discover after dinner.

However, dinner was for later. First there was a lunch to be dealt with and then the second visit of the day was to be undertaken. Or for those with sore backs, the first. And this was to a place called Tranquillity Eco Resort on the other small offshore island of Moso. This involved a fairly straightforward wet landing onto a golden-sand beach and the happy discovery that the eco resort was more to do with eco – and tranquillity – than it was to do with resort. Indeed, it was difficult to see that there was anything here at all, other than a rough stone jetty and an otherwise long unblemished beach edged with lush vegetation. In fact, as would soon become apparent, this place was more a dive centre than a regular resort, and as most enthusiastic divers in tropical climes are somewhat undemanding when it comes to associated facilities – like somewhere to sleep and somewhere to eat – the accommodation and general infrastructure could be characterised as minimal, extremely low-impact and discreet to the point of invisibility. And there didn't seem to be any patrons around either.

Well, Brian's back was now behaving itself quite well, and he lost no time at all in beginning to relish his situation. It really was beautiful here and clearly largely untouched. Furthermore, it was something of a refuge – for hawksbill turtles.

Now Brian, it has to be admitted, was quite well known for his propensity to wallow in the terrible plight of all wildlife in this world. However, he didn't actively seek out wallowing opportunities, especially if he had just been delivered into an earthly annexe of heaven. But here he was again, confronted, not of his own choice, with another dreadful manifestation of our impact on our fellow creatures, and in particular our terrible devastation of the world's population of hawksbill turtles.

These chaps are something special. Like most sea turtles they can grow pretty big – anything up to three feet in length. But what distinguishes them from other turtles is their rather elongated and tapered head that ends in a beak-like mouth, from which they derive their name. They also have a beautiful carapace, which combines amber, black and brown to spectacular effect. So far so good, but unfortunately, the hawksbill's diet means that it often feeds around coral reefs, just the sort of places where those seeking its meat or its carapace – for use in decorating various artefacts – can easily catch it. Which is one of the main reasons why the world's population of hawksbill turtles has plummeted over the last hundred years to the point where it is now officially critically endangered.

Many countries have exploited hawksbill turtles for their shells, and these include nations as diverse as Egypt, Colombia, China and Japan. And whilst these creatures' critically endangered status now means that it is illegal to hunt them in many jurisdictions, poaching continues as does the interest in certain countries for their decorative (and consumable) potential. And no prizes for guessing which country is the main culprit here. So, with continued exploitation by man, along with our unintentional impact, in the form of pollution, global warming, (nesting) habitat destruction and careless fishing practices, these turtles are in a very precarious state. Oh, and their eggs are quite tasty as well.

Yes, hawksbill turtles, as Brian already knew very well, needed an awful lot of help. And here at this eco resort, they were getting some help, and this came in the form of a turtle sanctuary, somewhere turtle eggs could be hatched in safety and then the young turtles reared until they were big enough to be released into the sea. This vital facility was just along the beach from the stone jetty, and soon Brian and Sandra were on their way to inspect it with a dozen or so other Caledonians. It turned out to be hidden within the island's vegetation – just past the resort's ultra-basic bar – and it was… well, a little disturbing.

The keepers of the sanctuary who were also the managers of its breeding programme were doing their best – but clearly with nothing like the required funding. They depended solely on donations – from the trickle of people who passed through the resort. This was clearly not enough, as was apparent in the Heath Robinson quality of the sanctuary's equipment, not least its use of rough and ready 'turtle tanks' and even the employment of old bath tubs for this purpose. Plainly they constituted a terrible environment for the poor baby turtles, creatures who normally live a solitary existence but were now being obliged to spend the first two years of their lives in the close company of dozens of other turtles and were very obviously hating it. They seemed to be spending most of their time trying to escape, not an easy task if you're just a diminutive turtle and you're trapped in a steep-sided bath.

Brian and Sandra weren't the only visitors to the sanctuary to feel rather upset. There were also some looks of despair on people's faces when later on two small turtles were released into the sea – both tagged awkwardly and both looking as though they might have opted for a return to one of those sterile baths. But what could be done? At least the young turtles here did stand some sort of chance, even if they had to endure an extended period of hell. It was just the poverty of the facilities and the feeling that they could be so much better – and the breeding programme upgraded as well. Which is why Brian brought up the subject of Britain's Department for International Development and the stupendous size of its budget. And what he suggested – to Sandra – was that maybe if it bought two fewer over-specified Land Cruisers each year or cancelled just one of those business-class flights for its ineffectual operatives every month, it could easily afford to bankroll this impoverished turtle set-up – probably indefinitely.

Sandra agreed, but made a suggestion of her own: that Brian abandon his pipe dreams and instead join her in a snorkel. Others were already in the water – just off the beach – and the prospect of immersion in water rather than in more dolour did sound attractive. So, after changing, and after avoiding the attention of the snorkel master and her insistence on having a snorkelling buddy, Brian and Sandra both slipped into the water separately and began to swim from the shore.

Oh dear. The water was very shallow and it remained very shallow. In fact it was so shallow, that Brian found himself crawling more than swimming and at the same time attempting not to plough furrows into his knees by dragging them over broken coral. It was quite clear, he thought, that this eco/dive centre resort catered for deeper-water scuba diving and not for depthless-water snorkelling just off the beach. Sandra, he then noticed, had already retired and had now joined a growing number of other defeated snorkellers who were just sitting in the surf and playing with their flippers. That was it. He would give up on attempting to find a reported moray eel and instead join the society of sedate surfers and maybe even find a sedate surfing buddy...

In the event he found Sandra (of course) and then between them they found a brown eared honeyeater (bird) – at the top of a palm tree. It was a suitable full stop to their visit to this island of Moso and to their shared concern for the situation of all those little turtles, about which they could do nothing at all. Other than maybe weep...

Well, back on board the *Caledonian Sky* it was soon time to plug into Trump-world again, not least because it might head off another bout of serious melancholia for Brian, following on from his skirmish with all that dolour back on Moso. And it did raise his spirits a little. Particularly when he listened to the great one speaking and realised – not for the first time – that his vocabulary was about as extensive as Brian's had been when he first started school. It was his store of adjectives that was the worst, which meant that if something wasn't amazing, beautiful, big, horrible, stupid, terrific, tremendous or unbelievable, he just didn't have a word to describe it.

Brian had considered this paucity of 'words that

modify nouns and pronouns, particularly by describing a quality of the noun/pronoun they are modifying' and had originally made a connection with a feature of George Orwell's *1984*. If he remembered correctly, that book described a ploy adopted by Big Brother's dreadful regime which was intended to close down people's avenue of thoughts. This was to ban more and more words, on the basis that if people didn't have a word to describe a thought then they couldn't think that thought – and life became ever more 'simple' in the Big Brother society. On a similar basis, was maybe Trump eliminating as many words from his own vocabulary in the hope that all Americans would follow his lead and eventually find themselves unable to express any sort of thoughtful and nuanced view – but just report that things were either horrible or tremendous?

However, Brian had now discarded this view. He now believed that Mr Trump was simply a man of very limited intellect, ignorant of any aspects of history, geography, science or the arts, incapable of understanding subtlety and nuance, and interested only in himself and not in extending his vocabulary – or his use of grammar, beyond that normally achieved at kindergarten. His narcissism had clearly acted as a brake on his development as a human being and on his interest in equipping himself with any real knowledge or even with another word for 'big' other than maybe 'huge'. But never, of course, 'colossal' – as in 'a colossal idiot of a president'. Or indeed as in 'a colossal idiot of a Brian'. Because, by raking up thoughts of *1984*, this melancholia-prone traveller had now stumbled into further thoughts, and these thoughts were all about 'the thought police'.

Yes, Brian, like many of his generation, had read books such as *1984* and *Animal Farm* and, early in his life, had become aware of the dangers of stuff like despotism, tyranny and totalitarianism. However, he had yet to read any work of literature that gave a similar warning about the insidious nature of political correctness, something that was too often regarded as a joke but something that even George Orwell might have felt compelled to write about. Of course, unlike the totalitarian 'this is the way to think and therefore the way to act', the PC equivalent would be more difficult to portray and even to identify to start with.

Nevertheless, maintained Brian, it is there all the time. It is the assumed way that all respectable people are required to behave in a respectable society such as in Britain. And (and this is the really insidious feature) how they are required to think. So when, for example, Brian was exposed to an advert on the telly with the mandatory diversity of its participants in place, he was not allowed to think that this was other than a good and proper thing. When he witnessed the normalisation of behaviour, attitudes and dress that were alien to his own culture, he had to welcome this and not regard it as an assault on his own probably rather more commendable culture. And if he was presented with a display of human rights that overrode his own country's hard-fought-for and long-standing civil rights, then he had to accept this as a welcome and proper development in the conduct of human affairs.

Well, the truth, he knew, was that this insidious and incessant assault on reason, common sense, identity, rationality and individuality is corrosive and just as evil as some of the worst manifestations of tyranny and despotism.

All people, he believed, should be free to think as they want. If therefore they want to reject in their minds all organised superstitions and indeed the bogus legitimacy of the world's established religions, then they should be able to do this. If they want to feel more empathy for their fellow species than for their fellow humans, then again they should be allowed to do this without being pilloried or abused. Indeed if they want to believe that the world was created by the interaction of resentment and stupidity, then so be it. And, to return to the real essence of this condemnation of PC thinking and the way it requires us all to act, if people want to believe that extreme tolerance, appeasement, meaningless human rights, futile attempts to rehabilitate monsters, 'respect' for individuals and cultures that deserve nothing of the sort, protecting people from offence, providing 'safe places' for students, and the designation of half the population of Britain as either vulnerable or in some way disadvantaged are all a load of bollocks, then as long as they don't do any physical harm to anybody else then they should be allowed to think this.

Brian knew very well the claim made some years ago that to destroy a society, one first makes it mad. He now believed that there was a concerted effort to bring about this madness by drawing all of society's citizens into the realm of political correctness. Quite simply, there was a desire on the part of those who are charged with responsibility for our society to standardise the way we think and therefore the way we behave, even when the prescribed way of thinking is patently stupid, short-sighted and... well, blatantly wimpish.

So, as far as Brian was concerned, the mantra should be: 'Sod quotas. Sod unearned respect. Sod unearned equality. Sod unearned rights. Sod bending over backwards so as not to cause offence. And sod political correctness'. And when we've done all that, as well as saving our society from collapse, we might even save one of our number from another episode of depression. Meanwhile, he would just have to rely on the restorative powers of a good dinner followed by a recital of a number of limericks...

Well, the dinner only made matters worse. A bit of a mix-up after the Caledonian Lounge briefing session saw Brian and Sandra sharing a table with four 'unknowns', a pair of couples whom they had seen in passing but knew very little about. Unfortunately they soon did. The first couple (who like the second, will retain a respectful anonymity) shared some of the features of those earlier inspected cave paintings. They were certainly indistinct in the sense of their presence, they were undeniably tedious in the extreme and they were disappointing in terms of their ability to mitigate the distressing impact of the other couple. These two comprised an ear, nose and throat doctor and his wife – who was an oversized puddin'. He, the ear, nose and throat man, was so self-obsessed that Brian wanted to puncture his glaring ego and his sickening self-assurance by making the point that, without orifices, he and many of his colleagues would be out of a job. Ear, nose and throat positions would disappear overnight, as would those for the world's gynaecologists and proctologists. However, he never got around to this, because his puddin' of a wife never stopped talking and actually managed to make the story about her Romanian nanny's surprise pregnancy last longer than a twenty-ounce gobstopper. (And yes, she could have managed one of those very easily.)

That just left the limericks – of which there were no less than five!

Sandra, back in their cabin, didn't appear to be too excited at the prospect of so many poetic gems. But Brian ignored the expression on her face – and a rather theatrical groan – and set about displaying his latest wares. These were (in order):

There was a young man from Moncrief
Whose todger was armed with sharp teeth
Well, strangely enough
It put women off
But it did help him once catch a thief

And

There was a young 'girl' made of plastic
With inserts of well-oiled elastic
Her purpose was clear
But I'll tell you, my dear
Her offerings were less than fantastic

And

There was a young lady from Weston
Who was open to any suggestion
She was almost hardwired
To give *more* than desired
But she'd always perform with her vest on

And

There was a young woman called Winnie
Who had this phenomenal innie
It looked like a purse
With its opening traverse
- Like the engine they put in a Mini

And finally

There was a young girl who'd rehearse
With a whip and with wants quite perverse
She loved in her act
Not her whip to be cracked
But instead what was quite the reverse

For a moment, Sandra said nothing. Probably because she couldn't really believe that last limerick. Yes, Brian just knew it. With that one, he'd almost nailed it. And the others weren't too bad either. Or rather, they were. They were cruder than ever – as was now being confirmed by a no longer silent Sandra. She'd clearly passed her shocked stage and was now intent only on informing her husband that maybe this cruise had 'enjoyed' more than enough of his hilarious limericks. And that was 'without any doubt whatsoever', if there were any more to come like that last one…

Brian just nodded, and he began to wonder whether he should try for five more tomorrow or possibly ease off to three. Oh, and wasn't it about time he penned one on Trump…?

10.

*B*rian awoke thinking about sand – and about one particular dump of sand. This was onto a reef in the South Pacific more than forty years ago, and the purpose of the dump was to raise a little of the reef above water at high tide. In this way it was then possible to build a small, above-water platform upon which could be placed a flagpole, and from this flagpole could then be flown the never-before-seen flag of the 'Republic of Minerva'.

He'd read about it – before he'd come on this cruise. How a Nevada-based real-estate millionaire, with a couple of mates, had set up something called the 'Phoenix Foundation', an organisation that was supposedly designed to create 'independent enclaves based on libertarian principles', but which in practice was more to do with carving out mini tax havens within which any sort of business could be set up – and particularly gambling casinos. Hence that initial attempt in 1972 to create the Republic of Minerva on a sunken reef – which was quickly stamped out by the authorities in Tonga – and then a more ambitious attempt, the next year, to set up a 'libertarian nation' in the newly independent Bahamas – which was equally unsuccessful.

However, if at first you don't succeed, then try, try again – this time in 1980 just as power is being transferred from the old colonial condominium of the New Hebrides to the newly formed country of Vanuatu. All one needs to do is identify a well-known local politician, give him some money and some arms (in exchange for concessions to install a casino and some other such laudable enterprises) and then get him to declare independence for what is the largest island in the former condominium, a place called Espiritu Santo. And it worked – or at least it did for a time. Independence was declared – for the new Republic of Vemerana – on 28th May 1980. Then the French government recognised the new nation on 3rd June! And then on 5th June that local (compliant) politician, one Jimmy Stevens, became the new prime minister, and the tribal chiefs of Espiritu Santo declared Philippe Allonneau, the former French ambassador, as the new king of the new republic (?), and its capital, Luganville was accordingly renamed Allonneaupolis!

So, slam dunk, and that guy in Nevada finally had the tax haven he wanted, which could now host all those libertarian ideals – and all those casinos and indeed 'any damned thing people want to do so long as it doesn't infringe the rights of others'. And no doubt this little slice of heaven on Earth would be with us till this day if only forces from Papua New Guinea hadn't turned up at the request of the new Vanuatu authorities and kicked Jimmy out – sometime in August of the same year. And rather than having tea with the new king every Tuesday afternoon, poor old Jimmy had to make do with his twenty-three wives and his forty-eight children, and he probably hadn't even been in power long enough to get his head on a new Vemerana stamp.

Well, the reason all this stuff was churning around in Brian's head, even before he'd lifted it from his pillow, was that this morning the *Caledonian Sky* would be arriving at the island of Espiritu Santo and indeed it would be berthing in what, for a very short time, had been Allonneaupolis, but was now once again just plain old Luganville. And frankly, how many times does one get the opportunity to visit anywhere that had such an ephemeral existence as a sovereign state – and in one's own lifetime as well? Answer: not very often. Which is why, when Brian did finally lift his head from the pillow he was so bloody annoyed. Because that was when he realised that his back was now so much worse. The prospect of actually seeing something of what had once been Vemerana, other than a dockside in Luganville, was already receding into the distance.

Brian made his condition – and his feelings – known to Sandra by employing an indecent word for excrement at the top of his voice. And then he let out a little whimper when he discovered how even using his vocal cords at the highest setting could induce pain in his back. He was stuffed, and Sandra would have to contemplate another unaccompanied visit ashore – while her husband stayed aboard, no doubt to divide his time between feeling sorry for himself and writing more of those damned limericks.

Well, that wasn't quite right. Brian did remain on board when Sandra left with virtually all of the ship's other passengers, but he managed to squeeze a little more into his morning than self-pity and poetic composition. In the first place he took himself to the sun deck, and from there was able to observe the captain of the *Caledonian Sky* putting members of the crew through a fire drill. He had assembled them on the Luganville dockside and he was timing them as they struggled to put on what looked like the heaviest firefighting clothing imaginable before running, with all their firefighting kit, to the other end of the dock. Fortunately, nobody suffered heatstroke in what was truly tropical heat, although whether this would have been the case if there had been a real fire as well (which are not unknown to be even hotter) he was not entirely sure. But, in any event, he felt reassured. All the guys taking part in this drill did very well indeed, even if they might have thought twice about taking part in any land diving...

Yes, Brian had met a fellow invalid on the sun deck, a fellow passenger who had once worked as a doctor in the Solomon Islands and who had once observed some land diving on Pentecost Island, another of the islands in the Vanuatu chain lying almost due east from Espiritu Santo. Well, Brian was keen to learn a little more about this rather strange ritual, of which he knew very little, and Andrew, the doctor, was keen to oblige him. He started by checking that Brian knew more or less what was involved: the construction of a tower from local timbers – from which the 'land dives' would be made – and the use of lianas tied around the divers' ankles so that when they launched themselves headfirst off the tower, they didn't plunge to their death.

Well, Brian did know all this, but he confessed as to

not knowing why anybody in their right mind would indulge in this precursor to bungee jumping – without the benefit of any of the safety arrangements that surround this modern manifestation of lunacy. Andrew, however, did know. It all began, he explained, with a legend. And the legend involved a young woman who ran away from her husband because… well, because he wanted it too often. And anyway, as it was here in Melanesia, the only place she could run to was into the depths of the forest. The trouble was that the over-sexed husband followed her in, and she then had to climb a banyan tree to avoid his unwanted advances. He, however, was not to be frustrated – and thereby left frustrated – and he climbed the tree after her. She then decided to jump from the tree, but being a woman, only after tying vines around her ankles to break her fall. He, however, being a man and probably pumped up in more ways than one, jumped off and as usual took no precautions. So, not surprisingly, he plummeted to his death. After which… the original land divers are reckoned to have adopted this daredevil practice in order not to succumb to the same fate. Andrew then went on to explain that it then developed into something that was associated with the annual yam harvest, in that good jumps ensured a good harvest. And, of course, there had always been that element of proving one's masculinity, even if it meant that one might break one's neck in the process.

That outcome was not impossible, reported Andrew. In fact, he had been told that before they dive the men settle their business affairs and any disputes just in case their head makes an inappropriate contact with the ground or with the tower. (If the liana is too long, it's the ground. If it's too short, it's the tower.) That said, fatalities are very rare, even though land diving has now rather moved on from being a ritual to being something of a tourist attraction. And it wasn't the only local practice to have taken this route – as Sandra was at pains to report when she returned from her trip ashore.

She had been to a place called the Nekar Custom Village (the name of which rather says it all). And here she and a host of the ship's other passengers had been treated to a greeting by some (amiable) warriors before being led into the village for a demonstration of 'village life, foodstuffs and crafts'. It was all very nice, she said, but one could not ignore the fact that all this stuff was for the benefit of... well, a load of tourists, and it didn't come over as entirely authentic. That said, she had been fascinated by the dozen or so ladies whose speciality was to create 'water music'. This they did, whilst dressed in grass skirts and standing in a small swimming pool, by beating and pounding the water with their hands to produce what Sandra could only describe as a unique sound. She imagined that this performance was originally conducted in the sea and not in a purpose-built pool, and it was originally conducted without an audience of middle-aged foreigners. Hence the feeling that this wasn't quite the 'real thing', even if the ladies did seem to be enjoying their vigorous slapping of the water and it probably beat preparing yams or washing the dishes by quite some way.

Anyway, she admitted, she was being just a tiny bit churlish, and she couldn't deny that quite a few of the passengers had really 'enjoyed' the kava on offer...

This is the drink made out of kava roots that is found throughout the Pacific region, and whilst not at all alcoholic it is nevertheless more than a little psycho-active. Indeed it can act as a sedative, an anaesthetic and a euphoriant, and it apparently induces in its imbibers an initial talkative period followed by muscle relaxation and eventual sleepiness. That, Brian had heard somewhere, was just what alcohol could do as well, but unlike alcohol, kava doesn't taste very good. He and Sandra had supped some in Fiji years ago, which is why Sandra had not tried it on this occasion. She knew she'd not have enough of it to get to experience its euphoriant qualities, but just enough to suffer its bitter, muddy taste and probably an unpleasantly numb mouth for some time thereafter. And anyway, there was a blue hole to visit, and she wanted all her faculties intact for that.

Yes, this was to be the finale of the visit to Espiritu Santo: a trek to a blue water hole in the jungle, where one could swim, jump into the water from a platform or indeed swing into the water on the end of a rope. Sandra was impressed with the water hole's setting but less so with the clarity of the water within it. And sadly she had to accept that her rope-swinging days were now past. Probably even with a pint of kava inside her, although maybe with enough gin and tonics...

It was this preference for a tasty alcoholic beverage rather than the local not so tasty tipple that caused Sandra to suggest to Brian that they report for lunch. If he could hobble along to the Bridge Deck restaurant, they could both have something to eat – and something to drink, probably in a wine glass. And that's what they did, with for company, this lunchtime, Paul and Lydia and a pleasant couple from Kent who were able to supply their table companions with the information that Espiritu Santo was supposedly the location for Rodgers and Hammerstein's *South Pacific*. Paul followed this revelation by reminding his companions that Espiritu Santo had served as a huge supply base for Allied forces in the Second World War, and then went on to explain how this aspect of its history had provided him with the sort of experience he would never forget.

He had been one of the ship's passengers who had eschewed a visit to the custom village and the blue hole in favour of an extended snorkel at 'Million Dollar Point'. And Million Dollar Point is where, after the war, the American forces dumped a huge amount of equipment into the sea rather than taking it back to the States or handing it to the locals. In fact, so much stuff was ditched in this place, reported Paul, that it should really be called 'Millions of Dollars Point'. And he'd now seen it for himself: an underwater landscape of discarded jeeps, trucks, bulldozers and tractors, and even things like bound sheets of corrugated iron and unopened boxes of supplies. It now, of course, represented something of a diver's paradise, but at the time very few people thought that discarding so much valuable kit in this way was a particularly blissful thing to do. Indeed, Paul had learnt that the locals thought that the Americans had gone mad and even some of the American soldiers doing the actual dumping wept as they were doing it.

So, why do such a thing? Why deny a store of what was largely non-military-specific equipment to the country that has hosted you during a war and whose native people have helped you in your struggle?

This was Brian's question to Paul, and Paul answered it by first pointing out that at the end of the war, there was an enormous amount of unused kit all across the Pacific. Getting the right amount of equipment into the right location had been simply impossible and there were now piles of poorly organised supplies just about everywhere. Some efforts had been made to sell this stuff or to make it available for post-war reconstruction, but there was just too much of it and the US military's priority was to get its troops home, not to concern itself with a load of redundant kit. Consequently, in what was still the New Hebrides, it was left to local commanders to make at least a token attempt to get the Franco-British administration to buy what was stored on Espiritu Santo. The administration refused, and this refusal didn't go down well. The Americans had already formed the opinion that the colonial presence in the New Hebrides was incompetent as well as being a relic of the past, and if the French and British wouldn't cough up any cash, then they wouldn't be getting anything. Which is why the US military's engineers built a ramp into the sea and drove all those jeeps, trucks and tractors into the water and then threw in so much more including the kitchen sink. And why the locals thought that the Americans were mad and why some of the Americans wept as they did it...

So, concluded Paul, the experience he'd so enjoyed this morning was a product of stupidity on a grand scale and maybe a comment on both the futility of war and the unintended consequences of dismantling the old world order. How might the Americans in Espiritu Santo have reacted, he wondered, if they were dealing with a new sovereign state rather than what could be characterised as a sclerotic vestige of a now waning colonial era? Although, there again, he proposed, had they not ditched all that kit, Espiritu Santo wouldn't be quite the magnet for divers that it now is – and the underwater attraction that the locals have been bequeathed has already proved itself much longer lasting than any jeep or tractor, and should, of course, last almost indefinitely. Which, finished Paul, was just possibly ironic but quite certainly a close cousin of serendipitous.

Brian agreed and then congratulated Paul on finding a place at the table for a word so testing as serendipitous – and at lunchtime. And then, a little while later, it was after lunchtime and time for an introduction to the Solomon Islands. This was to be in the form of a presentation in the Caledonian Lounge and, because of Brian's back, it would be accessed by Brian and his wife through the telly in their cabin. No point, he suggested to his wife, in risking further damage in the pursuit of knowledge, and no point either in denying the comfort of a bed…

So when Bob embarked on his presentation on the Solomon Islands, his audience in the lounge was smaller than it should have been by two. However, this didn't seem to dent his enthusiasm. On the contrary, he was almost as passionate about his subject as his leader Garth was about anything and everything. And he started with some fervently announced facts about this country towards which the *Caledonian Sky* was now steaming.

In the first place, he said, the country is both well named and misnamed; well named because the Solomon Islands comprise not only six major islands but also as many as 900 smaller islands, and misnamed because they were originally called *Islas Salomón* in the mistaken belief that they contained the sort of wealth ascribed to that King Solomon chap in the bible.

Staying with their geography for the moment, he then went on to inform his audience that the combined surface area of all those islands is more than 28,000 square kilometres (making the Solomon Islands over twice the size of Vanuatu) and that these islands lie to the north-west of Vanuatu and just below the equator, and the distance between the westernmost and easternmost islands is approaching 1,000 miles. So, he summarised, we have a big, fragmented archipelago, and not surprisingly, given its volcanic genesis, it contains a number of active and dormant volcanoes and it suffers from earthquakes and associated tsunamis. It also has a rich covering of rainforest vegetation which, again not surprisingly, has been seriously degraded by logging activities and this inevitably threatens its forty endemic species of birds.

This was all sounding far too familiar to Brian, as would the facts that Bob then laid out concerning the country's (European-era) history. This started with a visit in 1568 from a Spanish navigator by the name of Álvaro de Mendaña de Neira who as well as lumbering the place with its long-standing misnomer then left the field free for a more determined effort by a British captain in 1767, which would herald the arrival of explorers from Britain and from other countries such as France. This is where the déjà vu really kicked in for Brian. Because these incursions by Europeans led to the arrival of whalers, sandalwood traders and then the execrable blackbirders, who apparently made off with more than 30,000 slaves from the Solomon Islands to work in the cane fields of Australia and Fiji. Cue the arrival of missionaries, who made little progress in stamping out headhunting and cannibalism, and then the arrival of British governance which eventually made rather more progress in stamping out the slave trade. Yes, the evils of blackbirding prompted the British government to proclaim a protectorate over the archipelago's southern islands in 1893, which by the turn of the century had been extended to almost all of the archipelago and which then remained in place until self-governance arrived in the 1970s, followed by independence in 1978.

Bob did point out that this protectorate period of its history did have its moments, not least when the Japanese and Americans used the Solomon Islands as an extended battlefield. However he was rather keener to enlighten his audience on what has happened to the nation since independence – which might be summarised as 'going from bad to worse'.

Things started to fall apart in the late nineties when certain ethnic tensions began to emerge. These became so bad, with outbreaks of lawlessness, widespread extortion and out and out chaos – all leading to national bankruptcy – that in 2003, over 2,000 troops and police from Australia, New Zealand and twenty other Pacific countries arrived under the auspices of the Australian-led 'Regional Assistance Mission to Solomon Islands' (RAMSI) – to conduct 'Operation Helpem Fren'. And they did helpem their fren, by restoring order and assisting the country in getting back on its financial feet – sort of. Because the Solomon Islands is still at the bottom of the wealth league in the Pacific, and whilst it can probably avoid the title of a failed state, it has been referred to by some commentators as an 'unformed state', meaning that it has never been able to consolidate itself as a true modern nation even after decades of independence. And in Bob's opinion, that wasn't so surprising, as most of its inhabitants still lead very traditional lives in remote villages and the nation of the Solomon Islands is in many ways not much more than a colonial construct left to its own devices without any real sense of identity or coherence to see it safely on its way.

Well, this was all getting a bit depressing. Brian could feel that melancholia coming on. But worse was to come – in the form of the revelation that China (and Taiwan!) are increasingly manipulating the politics of the Solomon Islands through political funding, preferential loans – and whatever else is needed to forward their cause. In fact, it sounded from what Bob was saying as though the nation that is the Solomon Islands, if it were a person, would be classified as a vulnerable person – as well as a poor person. And even though the drawdown of the RAMSI presence has now reached the point where only overseas police now remain (and no troops), it was pretty clear that the country is still exposed to exploitation from without and exploitation from within – by the operation of a not entirely reliable or fully functional administration. Oh, and then there are its earthquakes and tsunamis.

Bob tried to finish on a high note – by explaining that, whatever its problems, the Solomon Islands was 'like what the Pacific islands used to be', and its village-based, traditional culture made it a fascinating place to visit (now that it was apparently safe to visit). Hell, he emphasised, it was why it had been included on the *Caledonian Sky's* itinerary, and why, in his mind, it could be regarded as nothing less than the highlight of the trip. Furthermore, he added, rugby union is played in the Solomon Islands, and, as everyone knew, only the good-guy countries play rugby. So where could be a better destination – for all sorts of reasons? Yes, where indeed?

Brian stared at a now silent telly and eventually turned to Sandra.

'Interesting,' he said. And then he became as silent as the telly because he had some thinking to do, thinking that had been prompted by that recently concluded lecture; not by its content but instead by the enthusiasm of Bob, its presenter. He had certainly started off enthusiastically, but then he had continued enthusiastically, despite much of what he had to say being somewhere between dispiriting and plain gloomy. The Solomon Islands story was hardly an uplifting one, but this hadn't diminished the enthusiasm in Bob's telling of it one little bit. It was as though his default setting was 'enthusiastic' and he could do little about it.

Brian gave this some thought, and quickly concluded that Bob must have been younger than he looked. After all, he was well aware that enthusiasm is a young person's thing. It's what drives young people to explore, to learn, to question and to discover, and it's what acts as a seemingly inexhaustible battery – for all that living they have to do as they discover even more. Unfortunately, however, it doesn't last. Exposed to the heat of experience, disappointment, failure and reality, it gradually melts away until it is little more than a puddle of 'passing interest'. Brian knew this well, as, like many people of his advanced years, he rarely if ever felt fervently enthusiastic about anything, but instead cautious or just plain suspicious. And if there was anything that didn't warrant either caution or suspicion – like the prospect of a cruise across the tropic of Capricorn, say – then he might just be able to assemble some serious anticipation or even a bit of buoyancy of mood. But never any genuine or even measurable enthusiasm.

It was sad. To realise one had now reached that point in one's life where to feel passionate about something was about as unlikely as being in receipt of some passion from a member of the opposite sex (good lady wives excluded, of course). And when one was confronted with so much uninterrupted enthusiasm in somebody such as Bob and when that enthusiasm on display seemed barely justified, it just made matters worse. One then had to resort to Brian's solution: put it down to youth. Even if it meant fooling oneself about the age of the enthusiast and then quickly identifying a distraction before one could question the bogus nature of one's solution.

Fortunately, a distraction presented itself immediately. It was Sandra informing her husband that

Outside the *Caledonian Sky*

Inside the *Caledonian Sky*

The old people's lounge

The preferable lounge

Just off Norfolk Island

On Norfolk Island

A safe distance from a volcano

Not quite such a safe distance from a volcano

Zodiacing

Turtling

The beautiful *Caledonian Sky*

The beautiful mangroves

Mudmen and matrons

The opposition

Honiara's take on political correctness

Rabaul (spot the *Caledonian Sky*)

if he looked out of the cabin window he would observe some prize-winning flying fish. And she was right. They had both seen these remarkable creatures before – fleetingly – but now there were dozens of them quite close to the ship and all of them were engaged in an aerial display that was nothing short of amazing. These chaps don't just leap out of the water and plunge back in after a few feet but they really do fly – and fly and fly. Here, some of them were managing anything up to fifty metres, which was quite remarkable. Although, as Brian would subsequently discover, by their using updrafts at the leading edge of waves, they can actually cover distances of up to 400 metres! In fact, he also discovered that in 2008, a Japanese television crew filmed one flying fish who remained airborne for forty-five seconds, which is probably more than some birds do, especially ostriches...

Of course, this impressive flying habit is not a recreational pastime for the fish but a behaviour that they've evolved to avoid being eaten. Which reminded Brian that it must now be time for him and Sandra to eat. He was therefore able to distract himself further by preparing himself for dinner, following which melancholia was successfully kept at bay by the dinner itself. It again involved 'the gang of six' and it also involved a lot of chatter. And it was good chatter. Lise, for example, paid tribute to all those ladies in the village on Espiritu Santo who managed to get through life without cling film. Lydia, on the other hand, challenged her companions to remember as many songs as possible from the film of *South Pacific* (which wasn't many).

Thor brought up Captain Cook by wondering out loud whether, if he'd beaten that Spanish chap to the Solomon Islands, he'd have called them the New Orkneys or the New Isles of Scilly – or maybe he would have had another aristocrat to flatter. And then Brian rather spoiled the party by asking why anybody convicted of a terrorist offence in Britain – and that's a terrorist offence of any sort – was ever let out of prison. And furthermore, he suggested (almost enthusiastically), what was wrong with bringing back or extending the scope of treason, so that all those scumbags who now constitute a genuine insurgency in Blighty can be dealt with expeditiously and effectively? This avenue of discussion proved to be a cul-de-sac, largely because Sandra trod on Brian's foot as she glared at him and then chose another avenue for the table talk by bringing up the subject of white plastic chairs and, through their ubiquity, whether they had the potential to become a new world currency for the benefit of all.

Brian capitulated and only returned to the offensive – in more ways than one – when he assaulted Sandra with his next crop of limericks back in their cabin. There were again five of them. They were:

There was a young man called Marcel
Whose gender was quite hard to tell
He looked like a *beau*
But as far as I know
He more often seemed like a *belle*

And

There was a young girl called Svetlana
Who once took a trip to Guyana
Whilst there on her tour
She got nicked by the law
And was charged with 'abuse of banana'

And

There was a young girl called Simone
Who quite liked to be on her own
What then she would do
Well… nobody knew
But she did often let out a groan

And

There was a young man from Stranraer
Who with girls would drive off in his car
And then he would say
'Shall we go all the way?'
But rarely they'd go very far

And finally

There was a young girl who was taught
That a sailor was worth less than nought
But strong rating Roy
And the shudder of joy
When his vessel docked in her home port!

Sandra's reaction to these latest works of genius was to put her head in her hands. Brian was unsure whether this was good or bad, but he did think that he could still do better.

Heck, he thought, he might even be developing some real enthusiasm for this stuff…

11.

ob's enthusiasm hadn't dimmed one little bit. And it was only seven o'clock in the morning.

He had joined Brian and Sandra for breakfast in the Castle Deck restaurant, and as they were attempting to feed on their chosen melange of various pig products and eggs, he was attempting to feed them as well – on even more facts about the Solomon Islands, and about one island in particular: Vanikoro. This was because this was where they would be visiting this morning – and, of course, because Bob had all that boundless enthusiasm. Indeed, such was his desire to educate them on all aspects of what was little more than a tiny speck in the Pacific Ocean that his own melange of pig products and eggs began to congeal before he got it into his mouth. He just wouldn't stop talking.

Anyway, what he had to tell them was, Brian decided, all rather interesting – even if a bit too didactic and a bit too early in the day. Inevitably, it started with some geography, and with Bob's attempt to place Vanikoro within the Solomon Islands archipelago – as discussed the previous day. It was, he told his students, about seventy-five miles south-east of the Santa Cruz group

141

of islands, which are themselves well to the south-east of the principal islands that make up the nation. And what this meant, he emphasised, was that Vanikoro is very much at the end of the line and very remote from the centre of power in this country. A bit like the Shetland Islands, he suggested, only even more remote and considerably smaller. Yes, Vanikoro has a land area of just sixty-seven square miles – and, Bob announced, it supports just 1,300 people.

At this point, Brian expected Bob to now talk about the people, but he hadn't quite finished on his geography. Because he was keen to point out that Vanikoro is actually not one island but two islands (both of which are populated) together with a number of (unpopulated) islets, all surrounded by one bloody big reef. Had a guy called Jean-François de Galaup, Comte de La Pérouse known this in 1788, his two vessels might not have struck this reef and he and his two crews might not have met their ends. As it was, he didn't, and consequently some of the matelots got eaten by the locals and those who were not consumed, even though they were able to construct a small craft and escape, were never seen again. And Bob had included this reference to this earlier navigator in his breakfast briefing because the disappearance of the *Astrolabe* and *La Boussole* (Monsieur de La Pérouse's two ships) stirred the interest of the whole French nation at the time and that interest was still there one hundred years later when Jules Verne dedicated a chapter of *Twenty Thousand Leagues Under the Sea* to the event. Oh, and there is a La Pérouse monument in the village on Vanikoro that would be visited this morning.

Well, with that dose of history out of the way, it was now time for Bob to move on to the people of Vanikoro, and to inform Brian and Sandra that of the total population of 1,300, only 800 are Melanesians – and the descendants of its original population – and the rest are Polynesians, who for the last three centuries have established a presence on the larger of Vanikoro's two islands, known as Banie.

This is where it got really interesting. In fact, Brian stopped eating his breakfast. He was so intrigued with Bob's tale of these 'newcomers' to Vanikoro. Because it appears that they originated in a place called Tikopia, which, if Vanikoro can be imagined as a shrunken Shetland Islands, then Tikopia can be imagined as an even more shrunken Faroe Islands. It is officially part of the Solomon Islands but it is 125 miles further east from Vanikoro and it is has a land area of just 640 acres! It is the remnant of an extinct volcano, but clearly not a very large one.

Well, according to Bob, Vanikoro's 500 Polynesians still identify with this place. This isn't surprising, he said. And this is because Tikopia society is unique. It has changed very little over the years and its members see themselves as upholders of ancient Polynesian traditions – while all those Melanesians in the Solomon Islands proper have lost most of theirs. This might be debatable, suggested Bob. But what cannot be denied is that the residents of that tiniest of islands have attuned their lives to the resources it can offer. For example, he went on, over 400 years ago, the entire population of Tikopia agreed to slaughter all their pigs – because they were consuming food that the people themselves could consume – and to replace pig husbandry with fishing. More significantly, they have developed and retained social controls that have kept in check their own reproductive urges and thereby their population. It has never risen much above a figure of 1,200, which, of course, is about as much as 640 acres can sustain.

This was what really caught Brian's attention: that all on their own, the population of a very small island in the Pacific had arrived at a sustainable lifestyle. Indeed, so successful were they in this endeavour that they have been cited as a model of sustainability – and a dramatic contrast to their counterparts on Easter Island who managed to sustain only an impressive collapse in their numbers as their ill-considered habits finally exhausted their environment.

That said, some of the Tikopians had felt the need to relocate themselves to Vanikoro. So their sustainable ways were maybe not that perfect. Nor, it seems, were their attitudes to assimilation into a host culture. And that was what also caught Brian's attention: the fact that the descendants of those still on Tikopia, who have now lived on Vanikoro for centuries, still identify with Tikopia rather than with their 'new' home. It was, thought Brian, what he was now observing for himself in Britain, albeit those resisting assimilation there and intending to continue to identify with their homeland were certainly not from Tikopia...

That could have been as far as Brian's sour musings on immigration went, but then Bob insisted on taking them further by telling his table companions that the

500 Polynesians on Vanikoro still spoke their own (Tikopian) language while the 800 Melanesians spoke a language called Teanu. Which, thought Brian, was a little too close to what he was encountering (as acceptable) far too often back in Blighty. He began to feel morose, and was only rescued from a downward spiral of despair by Bob's concluding remarks on Vanikoro which concerned another aspect of its native tongue. Because it appears that whilst there are 800 Melanesians speaking Teanu, there are four of them speaking another language called Lovono and just one of them speaking something called Tanema.

Yes, this tiny island had everything: an isolation from its neighbours, a history of cannibalism, its very own divided society – and a quartet of people who could talk only to each other – and one poor sod who couldn't talk to anybody. For this guy, thought Brian, it must be really horrible. It must be like landing on another planet where the locals communicate with their antennae and you can't even ask them to take you to their leader. Or, from Brian's personal, non-interplanetary experience, like living in a community of Glasgow taxi drivers. He could only feel sorry for that one Tanema speaker – and hope that he would at least make sure that he taught the Teanu speakers of Vanikoro all the Tanema expletives he knew before he finally popped his clogs and his language became extinct.

Anyway, with Bob's enthusiasm still ringing in their ears, Brian and Sandra now returned to their cabin to ready themselves for their visit to Vanikoro – and to prepare themselves for rain…

Yes, whilst Brian's back was a great deal better this morning, the weather was a great deal worse. There was a really lively wind out there that was stirring up the sea and this wind was intermittently laced with moisture. Brian and Sandra would therefore need to consider their waterproofs.

However, unknown to them, the captain of the *Caledonian Sky* was having to consider something else, and this was whether the rather energetic sea would still allow the ship's Zodiacs to get ashore at the chosen landing site, a village called Paeu on Vanikoro's west coast. Well, in due course, they did learn of this consideration. This was when Garth announced over the ship's PA system that the sea conditions were such that the captain was moving his ship to the more sheltered east coast of Vanikoro, where efforts would then be made to organise a landing at another village that was still ignorant of the potential arrival of a gaggle of advanced-years adventurers.

This gave more time to contemplate the employment of waterproofs but also more time to ponder the perils of what would apparently be a two-mile Zodiac ride in intemperate conditions across a reef that had already sent two French vessels to the bottom of the sea. Ultimately, both Brian and Sandra reconciled themselves to these possible perils, but Brian, unlike Sandra, decided that waterproofs would be redundant, as the weather, now that their ship was approaching the east of Vanikoro, was no longer moist in the least. Indeed, it was even possible to observe the 'pathfinder' Zodiac, manned by Garth and two of his helpers, as it raced to the shore to enable Garth to organise a reception at the replacement landing site – which, as would soon be revealed, was a tiny village called Usili.

Only a little while later, the Zodiac was returning – with its mission accomplished – and just minutes after its arrival back at the ship, the first of the Zodiac passenger trips to the island were under way. Brian and Sandra were in the third of the Zodiacs, which meant that there was no more than ten seconds between Brian sitting himself on the Zodiac's inflated edge and the non-moist conditions being replaced with some excessively moist conditions. It began to pour down – on Sandra's waterproofs and on Brian's T-shirt and shorts, and he was very soon soaked to the skin.

Matters did not improve when the Zodiac arrived at Usili. It was still pouring down and this meant that the wet landing on Usili's beach was the wettest by far on this trip, with the trees overhanging the beach offering no shelter but just larger drops of the wet stuff and an even deeper gloom to add to what was becoming a seriously gloomy day. The sun had clearly been called away to illuminate an entirely different part of the planet.

Anyway, all the Zodiacs had now arrived on the beach to decant their saturated shipments onto the shore and the assembled shipments started to make their way to Usili village proper. This was no more than thirty yards away, just beyond the beach – and it was in its 'natural state'. That is to say that because it had been recruited to the cause of international tourism only an hour before, there had not been time to organise a reception by the village warriors or an elaborate display by the village dancers. All there was were a few confused-looking villagers standing outside the dozen or so huts that made up their home and a rather slender-looking gentleman in a sports jacket standing next to Garth. He was the chief's son, and in the absence of the chief (who may have been leading an outreach programme to Vanikoro's Polynesians) he was the man who would welcome the unexpected visitors and receive a bagful of goodies from Garth as a recognition of his and his fellow villagers' impromptu hospitality. He said a few words – in presumably Teanu – and then Garth said a few more words – in English – and the island visit could now officially begin. In the rain.

It was very refreshing, thought Brian. Not the rain but the opportunity to see a little slice of Pacific Islander life in its unadorned state. It seemed… relaxed if a little basic and it did point to how people can live presumably contented lives with little if anything of what we regard as vital in the West. No Sky TV here. No gastropubs. No apps. No boutique gins. And no Ant and Dec. Instead there were just simple huts, a real sense of community, children with smiles on their faces – and all the rain you could ever want.

Yes. No way was it going to stop. And when Brian and Sandra joined some others who were going off to explore the forest and the mangroves that surrounded the village, he knew that his few clothes would remain wringing wet until such time as he took them off. It was just as well that it was still 'tropically warm'. It was also just as well that there were diversions to distract him from his waterlogged state. The first of these was a huge tethered pig, as, unlike in Tikopia, pigs are still reared in Vanikoro, and whilst not featuring in the locals' daily diet, their meat is still used for ritual feasts and the like. Unfortunately, animal welfare has yet to establish itself on this island, and that means that if you're a pig you get to spend your piglet youth pretty well unfettered, physically or otherwise, but when you grow up you're tied up – indefinitely. It seemed to Brian to be more than a little cruel.

So, the first diversion wasn't the best diversion. The second was much better. It was a flying fox. And it was on its own and when it flew into a palm it was feeding. Which could mean, Brian later discovered, that he had witnessed a Vanikoro flying fox and not the more common Pacific flying fox. (The former lives a rather solitary life and forages during the day; the latter is nocturnal and lives in colonies.) This was significant, because the Vanikoro flying fox was declared extinct in the 1990s and it wasn't until 2014 that it was rediscovered and found to be… not extinct. That said, there are no more than a few hundred of these animals, and they are inevitably critically endangered. It is just a matter of whether logging operations (on this out of the way island) will accomplish their final extinction or whether this will be opportunistic hunting – or just the usual plain fucking indifference to their plight.

Oh dear, Brian needed a further diversion. No problem. There were some fabulous fig trees in the forest. Then some parrots flying overhead. Then some astonishingly contorted mangroves down by the shore. And then some diminutive mudskippers, living fossils of sorts that can breathe through their skin and are therefore almost impossible to suffocate with a pillow… Oh, and the rain was proving to be a diversion as well. It was the sort that must have got Noah to Google ark-building in that it looked and felt as though it was never going to stop. No more than Brian's clothes were ever going to dry.

No matter. Because the visit to Usili and its environs was now drawing to a close and whilst Sandra had opted for a return to the *Caledonian Sky* and a large towel, Brian had opted for more moisture – in the form of a snorkel on Vanikoro's reef.

He arrived there in a Zodiac to find the scary Ingrid in another Zodiac – and an increase in the intensity of the rain that made him think seriously about aborting his snorkelling mission. It was now technically pissing it down, and one was all too aware of this when one had committed oneself to the water. It not only reduced the underwater visibility – by diminishing its illumination from above – but it also reduced the underwater temperature. This was distinctly and unpleasantly low, and when it joined forces with an unexpected strong current flowing across the reef, it had no trouble at all in convincing Brian that an early return to the Zodiac was a much better idea than remaining underwater and under the distinct impression that he should not have got off the inflatable in the first place. Despite all those beautiful fish on the reef…

When he finally got back to the *Caledonian Sky* he actually felt like a fish himself. He had spent a whole morning wetter than a haddock and as he sloshed his way back to his cabin he longed just to be dry again – and wet only in the mouth department, possibly with the aid of a wine glass, but not one containing water.

Mission accomplished. More than once and with the company of a couple called Sam and Jean who had joined Brian and Sandra for lunch. They were both good fun and both far less enthusiastic about anything than Bob was about everything. Brian thought they made excellent table companions and regretted that their respective paths hadn't crossed before. However, that was an inevitable function of the social arrangements on this ship. One was always wary of the company of certain of one's fellow passengers, and one therefore tended to seek out the company of one's preferred companions. But in doing so, one could easily miss out on the Sams and Jeans, those other passengers who would easily have earned that preferred-companion status.

One could also, of course, meet further promising company if one attended all the on-board presentations. And this afternoon, as the *Caledonian Sky* now steamed north-eastwards, there were two more of these on offer, one concerning fish and one concerning the South Pacific in films – with, in between them, a 'chocoholics' afternoon tea'. Well, that was all very well, but Sandra was feeling a little tired and Brian was feeling a little confused. Some random remark made by Sam over lunch had made him realise that he wasn't at all sure that writing limericks was doing much for his recurring melancholia and he had less idea than ever as to why he was experiencing this recurring melancholia in the first place. There was only one thing to do; while, back in the cabin, Sandra was enjoying a welcome siesta, he would provoke another bout of depression and then immediately after this write a few more limericks and judge how this affected his mood. And provoking another bout of self-indulgent gloom would be no problem at all, because that visit to Vanikoro this morning had supplied him with a perfect reason to feel deeply dismayed. It was, on this occasion, the growth of unreasonable expectations – when the inhabitants of a place like Usili village seemed to be able to get on very well without expecting much at all in terms of stimulation, possessions, opportunities and, most crucially, support.

Yes, Brian was off again, first of all conceding the point that we all have expectations. For example, we expect to be treated with civility by those around us. We expect to be abused or neglected by those who govern us. And we expect to receive what we have paid for, whether this is some sort of service or that inflatable exercise ball we ordered from Amazon. However, there are some, he believed – or maybe that should be a majority of humanity – whose expectations are both unreasonable and irrational, and who together represent a huge burden for all those others who are called upon to meet these expectations.

In Britain, this 'epidemic of expectations' now manifests itself in many forms and quite often is to be found in the realm of public services. So, Brian pondered, there are all those people who have happily ignored the unavoidable advice not to abuse their bodies but who then expect the NHS to jump to it when the time comes for the consequences of their self-neglect to be addressed, often in the form of prolonged and expensive treatment. And this is such a fundamental expectation for so many people that few will challenge it even when reminded that as often as not the recipients of the required treatment will have contributed nothing like enough to cover its cost. Other poor buggers will have done this, the same poor buggers who, through a national tax system, are now consistently paying to meet the cost of all sorts of unreasonable expectations that they themselves will never have.

They are unlikely to expect that it is 'quite OK' to have a large family that they cannot afford and that others will have to pay for. They are also unlikely to expect that a life of unemployment through choice is something others should be required to fund. And few of them would expect to be entitled to the sort of support that they themselves have never sought but is now handed out to all and sundry as a matter of course.

And this, Brian firmly believed, is where the expectation epidemic becomes a pandemic; when one observes what is going on all around the world and what, in so many countries, are now the entrenched expectations of their citizens, no matter how completely ridiculous these expectations might be. It is no secret, of course, which countries Brian had in mind here. It is those nations which, through embracing archaic and regressive beliefs and retaining an attachment to corruption as the currency of everyday life and to procreation as the national pastime, are either falling apart or are already in pieces. And don't just need help, but expect it…

Yes. Whoever coined the term 'the international community' needs his head slapping. Because now, all those unreasonable expectations, that someone will arrive to deliver the citizens of failing and failed states from the results of their own doings, will arrive as demands at the door of 'the international community'. And unfortunately, it is neither a real community and nor is it comprehensively international. In fact, it's just North America, Europe, Australia, New Zealand and maybe Japan, a disparate but limited number of countries which could well do without the demands with which they're now constantly assailed.

And worse, believed Brian, was that those expectations in the buggered-up bits of the world now include the right to move to the non-buggered-up bits, especially those close-by bits like Europe. And not only is this unsustainable, unreasonable and plain wrong, it is also seen by many of those who make this move as a fulfilment of a valid expectation and nothing more than that. So a refugee in Germany can openly complain that his children are becoming 'Western', when he'd brought his family to this land to have them educated, not for them to become German...

Brian had heard that refugee, and he had thought at the time that this is exactly what happens when expectations bordering on the preposterous take root. They either lead to disappointment when they cannot be met, or if they are met – always at someone else's cost – they are not appreciated and they quite often lead to further and even more preposterous expectations. They also, of course, lead to some serious resentment in the minds of those called upon to satisfy these myriad expectations, whether these are all those responsible taxpayers at home or every last responsible citizen in that small group of countries that have somehow been press-ganged into 'the international community'.

So, in the interests of reaching the very bottom of his depressed state, Brian concluded his musings by confirming in his mind the belief that excessive and unreasonable expectations now constitute one of the very worst ailments in the modern world. Quite simply, they license appalling behaviour by shifting the consequences of this behaviour to someone else. And only when everybody wakes up to the iniquity of all this nonsense will people take responsibility for their own actions and for the fallout of their own often dysfunctional cultures. And at about the same time, thought Brian, Hell will be freezing over very nicely.

OK. It was now time to write those new limericks. So that's what Brian did. And when he had, his melancholia had lifted a little. Not enough to be replaced by euphoria but definitely enough for him to relish the prospect of a dinner. And he thought he could even manage another one of Garth's debriefings before he dined. That, however, was before Garth had begun to wax lyrical about the 'real adventure' represented by the day's earlier soaking and had then gone on to proclaim that in seventy-two hours' time, one of his team would be announcing the winner of the ship's limerick competition! Yes, as a tribute to the sailors who accompanied Captain Cook, all the *Caledonian Sky's* passengers were now being invited to write and submit as many limericks as they liked – concerning any aspect of the Pacific Ocean – with the intention of finding the very best limerick and then rewarding its author in just three days' time!

Bloody hell! This news almost ruined Brian's subsequent dinner – but not quite. And, much to Sandra's dismay, it did nothing to dissuade him from parading those five further limericks he'd prepared earlier on. These were:

There was a young chappie called Harris
With a 'warhead' the size of Polaris
And one hardly need say
That when brought into play
It would harden like plaster of Paris

And

There was a young lady from Bute
Whose interest in balls was acute
When meeting a stud
Just as soon as she could
She'd go for his low-hanging fruit

And

When Annie's libido was 'started'
It was not for the weak or faint-hearted
It would lovers so strain
That they'd end up in pain
- Or as one of the dearly departed

And

There was a young girl who liked trees
But more so her partners to please
In pursuit of this cause
When buying new drawers
She would check how they looked round her knees

And finally

There was a young lady called Chloe
Who decided to wax her below-ee
But the wax was all wrong
And the hair grew back strong
So that Chloe then needed a mow-ee

Brian looked at Sandra for her verdict. It came in the form of a short statement.

'Brian,' she said, 'I hope to God you're not thinking about entering that limerick competition.'

But, of course, he was…

12.

*I*t was nine in the morning, and the *Caledonian Sky* was still steaming north-eastwards. This wasn't surprising. Getting from yesterday's Vanikoro to today's destination – an island called Santa Ana – involved a voyage of no less than 266 nautical miles. This Pacific Ocean, thought Brian, is a bloody big place, and even within the confines of the Solomon Islands, the distances are enormous. Which, he also thought, is not the word one would apply to Santa Ana, a coral island located at the eastern end of a bigger island called Makira – and measuring just 3.5 miles by 2.8 miles. It was another speck in the vastness of this endless ocean.

It was also a place that one of his breakfast companions had been to before. Yes, Andrew, the doctor who had previously worked in the Solomon Islands, had, years ago, taken the opportunity to visit this place – in order to learn about a rather unusual German who had lived there. He was now telling his fellow fast-breakers what this guy was all about and what made him so unusual if not unique, and this tale started with some further information about Santa Ana itself.

It was, according to Andrew, an island supporting a population of just 1,500 people, all of whom speak a language called Owa (which is why the official name of the place is Owaraha). This language together with its associated culture is shared only with the people who live at the eastern end of the nearby Makira island, and this, Andrew pointed out, would clearly make Santa Ana's residents very protective of their identity and probably very resistant to any sort of external influences. However, despite their literally insular nature, the inhabitants of this tiny island, back in 1912, accepted into their midst a German fellow by the name of Heinrich Küper, and one of the inhabitants actually accepted him into her bed. Yes, Heinrich married a local woman, a lady who was blessed with the name of Kafagamurirongo, providing her, of course, with one new syllable for every day of the week...

Anyway, Heinrich was entirely serious in his intentions, and with Mrs KK went on to have four children, thereafter becoming the only white person in history to reach something called the *arafa* (high person) status in Melanesian society.

In fact, this bloke adapted entirely to the local island culture and, according to Andrew, this meant that he soon began to mistrust European influences as a whole and European missionaries in particular. He warned his fellow islanders that, with their bibles, they would seek to dismantle the traditional structure of their society and incubate moral breakdown and even conflict. Fortunately, no European lawyers turned up while he lived there, as what he would have said about them would probably be unrepeatable.

Brian found this all fascinating stuff, not least

Andrew's revelation that this guy's grandchildren and great-grandchildren still live in the Solomon Islands, some in the capital, Honiara, and others on Santa Ana itself. It was very rare, he thought, that anybody with a European cultural background would so enthusiastically embrace an entirely different culture, but it was probably even rarer that this 'alien' culture would then respond so well to this unsolicited embrace. Especially when the guy with his arms around you was a white one. It was, thought Brian, a really uplifting insight into human nature (which for Brian, of course, was about as rare an event as Herr Küper's successful integration into Melanesian society).

Yes, it was time for Brian to revert to norm and either to identify something to be annoyed about or something to worry about. And in the event, directly after breakfast, he chose the worry option. He decided to fret about the need to produce not just his daily diet of limericks, but now a clutch of Pacific-themed limericks that were intended to be exposed to a no doubt demanding audience in two days' time. There was only one thing to do: (again) ignore this morning's presentations and, before the *Caledonian Sky* arrived at Santa Ana, write as many damned limericks as possible. After all, others were probably busy with their pens already, and they didn't have to produce the indecent stuff on top of the Pacific stuff. Unless, of course, like Brian, they had been captured by the need to produce five-lined, rhyming obscenities every day...

Well, that might never be known, and meanwhile, after a full morning's further steaming, the *Caledonian*

Sky was now dropping anchor off Santa Ana. Soon the Zodiacs would be deployed, and Brian's back would be put to the test yet again as, with Sandra, he was whisked ashore to make a wet landing at one of Santa Ana's two villages, a place called Gupuna – and the very place in which Heinrich Küper had made his home! Would it be possible, thought Brian, to discern a tinge of white in the local population? And then he thought that this first thought was bordering on the racist and it was at least pretty offensive. So he didn't share it with Sandra and instead concentrated on the approach to this next new island. Under a brilliant blue sky, it looked just like an idyllic Pacific island, and the welcome awaiting the Zodiacs' passengers looked... interesting.

The inhabitants of Gupuna, unlike the inhabitants of Usili on Vanikoro, had been given plenty of notice of the arrival of their guests, and they had clearly used this notice period to organise something special. To start with this involved their stationing some gentlemen on the beach which separated Gupuna from the ocean and which, of course, was where the Zodiacs' passengers would be wet-landed, one Zodiac at a time. These guys' job was to 'regard intensely' the advance of each inflatable and, as its complement of passengers then attempted to secure the beach without coming to grief in the surf, charge at them with spears raised and with an expression of menace on their face. They didn't look to be playacting, even though, fortunately for the Zodiacs' passengers, they were. Or at least to the extent that they weren't likely to actually spear anybody intentionally – with malice aforethought and all that.

Brian was quite impressed – if a little inappropriately amused. He knew these warrior challenges were now more of an honour than they were a warning, but he couldn't help thinking about what might be going on in the 'warriors'' minds. Was there in there a mix of resentment and embarrassment, or was it something closer to euphoria? Was being licensed to charge at white people with a spear a bit like having a big meal of pork, a bellyful of kava and a really good, shuddering ejaculation all rolled into one? He would desperately have liked to know, but he knew he would be left to make his own judgement on the matter, probably based on what he had still to observe when he entered the village. Because, in the village, preparations were under way for a 'cultural ceremony' involving music and dance…

The village was lovely. It was a very large village and it had at its centre a huge 'village gold', a huge cleared expanse of hardened sand on which the cultural ceremony would be performed. Brian knew this, because to one side of this space had been assembled the village's entire stock of plastic chairs, on which a number of middle-aged bums could be placed in order to spare twice that number of middle-aged legs. Furthermore, surrounding the open area, and clearly designed to embellish it, were some 'tropical Christmas trees', cut saplings thrust into the ground and decorated with flowers and palm leaves. In fact, over breakfast, Andrew had mentioned that the one European tradition that Heinrich Küper had insisted on observing was Christmas, and to this end, each year he would arrange a Christmas dinner for the entire village and he would make a Christmas tree using the leaves and branches of local trees. So, could what Brian had interpreted as tropical Christmas trees be a living legacy of that German from the past? It didn't matter one way or the other really, but in Brian's mind, little puzzles like that were a darned sight more interesting than much of what now passes for interesting in the world of celebrity, the world of superficiality (otherwise known as 'metropolitan life') or the world of infantility (otherwise known as 'soshul meeja').

So, returning to Gupuna village, all the bums were now seated, the village band was tuning up, and finally, on the command of the village chief, a conch-shell trumpet was blown and the cultural ceremony got under way. First on stage were a dozen or so men, the sort of men who looked as though they'd never seen a burger in their lives and wouldn't ever need to join a gym. They were dressed in skirts made from slender palm leaves (over underpants of various colours) and they were decorated with fronds and flowers about their heads and arms, but otherwise they were uncovered. And what they had on show were the sorts of bodies we no longer see in the West, bodies that were still as they were designed to be; supple, sculptured, toned and entirely uninflated. They were, of course, beautiful, and their owners needed to do little other than shuffle around in time to the band's music to provide a striking display. Oh, and they looked almost to be enjoying themselves as well.

Next it was the women's turn. They filed onto the village square to take over from the men, and then embarked on their own sort of shuffle-dance, one, Brian thought, that had a little more order and complexity

163

than that of their male counterparts. They were wearing a little more than their male counterparts as well. Their costumes were made up of grass skirts (over colourful fabric skirts), close-fitting bodices made of palm leaves, elaborate frizzy headpieces, frizzy armbands and lots of necklaces and bracelets. Some of them were beautiful, some not quite so beautiful, but few if any of them were wearing even a hint of a smile. Brian could not decide whether this was part of their culture or a reflection of their being less than enthusiastic about having to perform before a strange audience. Or it might have been the tightness of those bodices…

Act three was the 'matrons' mazurka'. Only, of course, it being a group of older women performing it, it was more a meander than a mazurka, and its tempo was no more than 'dead slow' and 'stop'. It was however interesting, if for no other reason than the ladies in this seniors' troupe were wearing just their normal Sunday best, but had on their heads cones of some sort of white fabric. And for Brian, this had an inevitable and entirely disrespectful result, in that he could not now think that they were doing anything other than the traditional 'dunce-dance' of Santa Ana.

Fortunately, before he could share his irreverent thoughts with Sandra, the climax of the ceremony was beginning to overtake the matrons' performance, and this climax was the 'mud-mask dance'. It started with the arrival of the 'mud men', male villagers wearing just a loincloth around their loins and a long envelope of palm leaves on their heads, with the loincloths, the headgear – and their entire bodies – coated in orange-brown mud! It must, thought Brian, have taken them hours to prepare and it would take them quite some time, after the event, to get all that stuff off. Although maybe it would be less time for the youngster who was similarly daubed and who was now being shepherded towards the not-quite-redundant matrons by his mud-covered minders.

There was no commentary on this dance, but Brian had earlier overheard a remark about it being a representation of what the Melanesians had suffered, both at the hands of the Micronesians and the Polynesians who, rather than rejoicing in their all being Nesians together, tended instead to be somewhat aggressive in their habits – particularly towards the Melanesians. Well, as far as he could make out, the mud guys were the Melanesians (although why they needed to 'orange up' he wasn't quite sure) and they were under attack from their non-Melanesian neighbours. And this suspicion was reinforced when some new guys turned up – with spears and with spikey palm-frond skirts – and with comprehensively blacked-up bodies! Because, as far as Brian could tell, these were the Polynesians or the Micronesians or some sort of not-wanted-here-nesians, and they were looking to take that muddied-up youngster from his muddied-up (Melanesian?) guardians.

At this rate, thought Brian, he would soon be receiving invitations to provide voice-overs for any number of anthropological programmes on the telly, starting with 'Brian on Native Nesians and their Nefarious Nature'. Or… he might just admit to himself that he hadn't a clue what was going on, but that it was all very entertaining, especially when the blacked-up guys seemed to be frustrated in their attempts to abduct the muddy youth. And that was another thing. What could be more entertaining than seeing black guys making themselves even blacker when, at the same time, white Morris dancers back in England can't even blacken their faces (as they have been doing for hundreds of years) without being abused by a bunch of ignorant tossers?

Anyway, it had all been great fun, and whilst its authenticity could always be questioned, this 'cultural ceremony' did seem to have gone down well with all the non-performing villagers – and particularly with the kids in the village who had sat around enthralled. And as for the visitors – including Brian – well, it had clearly left them feeling happy and privileged, privileged to have witnessed such a remarkable and such a ridiculous reminder of the past, a reminder of the times in the not too distant past when the spears carried by many of the performers would have been used in earnest. So, all in all, a fabulous display and not in the least toe-curling, but just a little puzzling in certain respects. Like how did the mud guys see where they were going (there didn't seem to be any eye-holes in their mud-covered headwear), how did the band produce such fabulous music with a load of what looked like cobbled together instruments, and how did the Adonis-types at the beginning of the performance manage to look so cool wearing palm leaves around their Calvin Kleins? (And Sandra was just positive that that's what they were…)

Brian soon accepted that these puzzles would remain puzzles, just as he accepted that a post-performance, one-kilometre walk to a lake 'over coral rocks with slippery tree roots in places' could be an ask too much for his back. Accordingly, he and Sandra settled on a walk around the village and an inspection of the many handmade artefacts that were being offered for sale. Having then made a suitably embarrassed purchase from a gentleman who seemed more bemused at the transaction than pleased with it, the un-intrepid couple then got themselves ferried back to the *Caledonian Sky*. There, Sandra engaged in some in-house laundry activities and Brian engaged in another stint of melancholia. It just overtook him, he explained to his wife, and its genesis, he proposed, could only have stemmed from Herr Küper's suspicion of missionaries. Because what had sent him into a tailspin of gloom were his thoughts on religion…

It was a subject he'd thought about many times before. But that wasn't going to stop him thinking about it again. And he started on his path to misery by recalling that there was no pastor and no place of worship on the *Caledonian Sky*. There was a doctor on board and people who could navigate the ship, and others who would look after all the physical requirements of its complement of passengers. But there was no one to attend to their spiritual needs and no place for them to gather to worship a god. And strangely enough, these deficiencies in the *Caledonian Sky's* offerings didn't seem to matter. Eighty-eight mostly British people could exist at sea for days on end without any tangible manifestation of an organised religion and none of them could be observed to be falling into depravity as a result of this absence of religious guidance or religious practice.

This was hardly surprising, but it did mean that Brian found himself embarking on another voyage into not just the absence of religion but the 'evils of religion'.

This was, of course, an indigestible term for many and it ignored all the good works performed by religious institutions in terms of their provision of things such as hospices and schools and places of shelter. It also ignored the succour they provided to literally billions of people on this planet. However, in Brian's mind, those various good works were comprehensively overshadowed by these organised religions' impact on modern mankind, and that succour was just a blinker...

He would be the first to admit that in a former world of ignorance, full of the unexplained and the mysterious, it was only natural that primitive beliefs and all sorts of superstitions would eventually be shaped into organised religions. It was also quite understandable that the developing religions would be harnessed by the powerful and by a bunch of chancers for their own ends. Yes, whilst these religions might provide a set of beliefs concerning the nature of the universe and its supposed creator and they might provide their followers with a moral code that was designed to govern the conduct of their lives, they also furnished those in charge and the clerical elite with all sorts of opportunities. With religion they could maintain control over the gullible masses and at the same time cement their positions of power and thereby secure their access to wealth.

So, when a chink in that curtain of ignorance let in a ray of enlightenment that would eventually lead to such an advancement in mankind's understanding of the universe that all religions would be relegated to the level of embarrassing myths – they weren't. And maybe this rejection of insight and understanding wasn't just the work of a manipulative establishment. Maybe religions had so inveigled their way into the human consciousness that they just couldn't be dislodged, and in the face of an overwhelming challenge they burrowed in even deeper. So that we now have the majority of people on this planet consumed by a madness, a majority who are prepared to accept everything religions tell them, no matter how preposterous this is and how much it flies in the face of informed, rational thinking.

Of course, Brian thought, this madness wasn't universal – quite. There were corners of the planet where domesticated religions such as the Church of England or an entire absence of religious beliefs allowed people to live their lives peacefully, rewardingly, rationally – and spiritually – without resorting to any forms of bigotry, rivalry, blindness or tripe. Indeed, that was why the eighty-eight souls on this ship, in the absence of a religious 'referee', hadn't fallen into conflict or debauchery. And, in Brian's mind, that was more than a flippant observation.

In the first place he now believed that secular wars had long ago lost out to religious conflicts in this world. By simply belonging to one religion, one could become the natural enemy of those of another religion. Or, as is apparent across one whole swathe of the world, one can even become the mortal enemy of somebody of the same religious persuasion – who is not in the same 'gang'. Furthermore, these animosities are not confined to name-calling or displays of disrespect. They more often than not now erupt into real bullets-flying, bombs-exploding conflicts. And in these violent encounters it will do no good whatsoever to claim no religious allegiance at all. As any secular type kidnapped in the Middle East will confirm.

So religions cause wars. Not, Brian conceded to himself, a new idea. But possibly worse than this is their impact on human nature – and this goes back to that observation that none of the passengers on this ship had fallen into debauchery. Or, for that matter, any behaviour that could be described as intolerant, selfish or even judgemental. This was the second reason that he believed that his observation about the conduct of the passengers on this ship was not at all flippant – but rooted in fact.

This was because he had learnt before he had come on this cruise that a recent extensive study had demonstrated that 'pious' people, the sort who attend churches, temples, synagogues and mosques and are overtly and seriously religious, are not such 'nice' people compared to those who do not. They tend to be less empathetic, less generous, more eager to punish and generally less desirable individuals – whether still children or fully-formed adults. This, in Brian's mind, was hardly surprising. After all, it was all too easy to visualise that poker-faced, righteous-sounding zealot being responsible for some of the worst acts of intolerance and misogyny one can imagine. And if there is any difficulty in imagining this connection at a personal level, then one only has to consider the same phenomenon at a national level, where it is crystal clear that the more religious a nation is in its governance and in its culture, the worse it is in its attitude to women, minorities, foreigners, other religions, natural justice, the natural world, the natural environment – and enlightenment in all its forms.

But to return to that individual who is pious – but behaves disagreeably – it is now believed, through that recent study, that this is because of something termed 'moral licensing'. This is the tendency of people to use 'something good' to justify 'something bad', often without even realising they're doing so. Consequently, the religious types come to believe that they have done 'something good' simply by being religious, and that this gives them the licence to do 'something bad' – like becoming miserable bastards who feed on intolerance like a drug.

So, in Brian's mind, the conclusion was inevitable. Religions are not just ridiculous, obsolete, a cover for questionable cultural practices, counterproductive in the way we care for the Earth, and the cause of most of the deadly conflicts in the world today, but they are also a genuinely negative influence on the way we develop as kind and considerate human beings. And if that didn't 'elevate' them to the status of evil, Brian didn't know what did (charitable work excepted). And wasn't their suffocating embrace of mankind one of the most depressing things one could imagine. Oh, and what's more, because of their procreative habits, the religious in the world are set to outnumber the non-religious and ultimately to consign them to extinction. And that was possibly an even more depressing thought…

It was therefore fortuitous that Sandra promptly terminated Brian's latest immersion in gloom by reminding him that there was a dinner to prepare for and that he also had to give some consideration to attending a post-dinner dance. That really did the trick, and soon Brian was groomed and dressed for dinner and firmly of the opinion that he had already had all the dancing he could manage for one day. Instead, he would prefer to work on a few more limericks – and discharge a further five. When he relayed this decision to Sandra she seemed relieved and appalled in equal measure. And subsequently, over dinner, she seemed just exasperated. This was when Brian offered another of his opinions on Donald Trump. This one concerned his apparent desire to dismantle and generally poison any relationship with any country that had, until his tenure of the presidency, acted as one of his country's allies. It was as though, suggested Brian, he was doing a Pol Pot: destroy everything and then rebuild anew. Which was all very fine until one remembered that this guy hadn't a clue how to build anything, other than possibly a growing fascination around the world in his clumsy, ignorant, ill-mannered and vulgar behaviour.

It wasn't, of course, vulgar in the same way that Brian's limericks were vulgar, as he was now keen to demonstrate when he and Sandra had returned to their room. The demonstration took the following form:

'Sandra,' he announced, 'what do you think of these?' And then he proceeded to read the latest batch. These were:

There was a gay lady called Penny
Whose girlfriends were almost too many
Then her tryst with those ewes
Hit the nine o'clock news
And she soon found she didn't have any

And

There was a young woman from Frome
Who once went for an intimate groom
The groomer was male
And the end of this tale
Is just what you'll no doubt assume

And

There was a young woman called Sophie
Whose whatsit had won her a trophy
One has to deduce
That she charged for its use
And the fee charged was far from a low fee

And finally

There was a young lady called Sally
Who devoted her life to the ballet
She loved all the dance
And those men in tight pants
And their clinches were right up her alley

As Brian finished the delivery of this last ode, Sandra commented without even being asked.

'All revolting, and poor, poor, passable and adequate in that order,' she announced. 'If you want to win that limerick competition, you're going to have to do better than that.'

Brian gulped. He knew she was right. And he also knew he was losing his focus. He was trying to write too many limericks. He'd better sort himself out or he wouldn't stand a chance.

Or maybe he should just pray…

13.

*F*or the last two days, Brian and Sandra's experience of the Solomon Islands had been one of 'what the Pacific islands used to be like'. Both Vanikoro and Santa Ana had given them a taste of the traditional life that had been practised in this part of the world for centuries. However, that was all about to change, because this morning the *Caledonian Sky* would be *docking* (without the need for Zodiacs) in a place on the north-west coast of the island of Guadalcanal, and this place was Honiara, the capital of the Solomon Islands and a 'city' of 85,000 people.

Brian had already done a little reading on this 'metropolis', and he knew that it had acquired its national-capital status only when the British decided to make it the administrative centre for what was then the British Protectorate of the Solomon Islands. That was in 1952 – and when the British recognised that its infrastructure had been fairly well developed by the Americans during WWII (in the wake of their use of the whole of Guadalcanal as a place to hammer their hapless Japanese adversaries). Further development then followed, with Honiara receiving the lion's share of all the investment poured into the archipelago prior to independence, even though its population was then a very small one. This, of course, taken together with its role as an administrative centre, encouraged a sizeable growth in the number of its residents, and consequently it now represents an 'urban blot' on the otherwise very traditional, rural landscape of the whole nation. That said, with all that investment, and even taking account of the more recent civil disturbances, it would probably be a fairly well-sorted urban blot. Or so Brian thought...

Well, to start with, there was a properly functioning, if not very pretty, dockside. Brian and Sandra studied it from their balcony as, after breakfast, they waited for the call to disembark. At the same time, they fretted about the current level of heat and humidity, and what this might mean for their forthcoming city tour. It really was... well, tropical, and in due course both of them were greatly relieved when they were safely installed onto minibus number three (out of four), and could there begin to savour this vehicle's air-conditioned interior. 'Expedition cruising', they believed, did not necessitate an undue degree of discomfort when the expedition was being conducted through an urban environment. Particularly when it was being conducted at such a pedestrian pace...

Yes, as became apparent as soon as the convoy of minibuses left the dock area, Honiara's few vehicular arteries were completely clogged with traffic – to the point of thrombosis-inducing inertia. Nothing moved, or if it did – eventually – then it was at a pace that couldn't even be described as truly pedestrian. It was more like 'seriously hobbled'. And whilst this meant that most of this city visit would be spent in a bus, it also meant that the occupants of the buses would have all the time they needed to acquaint themselves with the roadside fabric of this tropical metropolis.

It was, decided Brian, the sort of fabric one would not have chosen to impress. It was tired-looking, faded and bland – and it certainly showed no evidence of all that investment in the past, or indeed little of any investment in the present. This was clearly an impoverished capital of an impoverished nation, an assessment of its status that would be firmly reinforced in the capital's National Museum. An arrival at this institution was secured after about three days of travelling... or was that three quarters of an hour, and it just felt like three days? Anyway, as national museums go, it was modest to the point of being bashful. It definitely didn't draw attention to itself, and its collection of old photos, old weaponry, body ornamentation and other assorted artefacts (all housed in one room) was distinctly self-effacing. There was actually rather more in the museum's gift shop, including some sharks made out of wood and designed to accommodate human skulls. Brian almost bought one, but Sandra lost no time in reminding him that any one of them would be far too big to transport back to Britain – and that, when back in Britain, there was very little likelihood that they would be able to procure any suitable skulls to fill it. She hadn't seen one in Waitrose for years.

So that was the museum and the museum shop ticked off the list – and, as the buses left the museum (very slowly), Brian ticked himself off. He knew he had regarded the museum's display with what amounted to disrespect if not contempt, and he had not given its custodians any credit whatsoever for what they had achieved in the face of national destitution and some serious civil unrest. So, well done, the museum, and if he ever got there he would make every effort not to be quite so scornful about the tour's next 'point of interest': Honiara's long-established Central Market.

Well, he and all his fellow shipmates did get there eventually, and what they found was that the market was contained within a large, open-sided building near the waterfront, and that this building was full of lots of people and lots of produce. However, as Brian and Sandra both noticed as they entered the building, there was something that it was not full of. It hit them immediately. Because it really was so obvious. In this busy central market there was no… bustle. There was no hubbub and no vibrancy – nor a great deal of commerce going on either – but just a lot of listless-looking people sitting behind some rather pathetic displays of groundnuts, vegetables and bananas and seemingly immersed in either lethargy or apathy to pass away the time. So Brian was immediately at it again: being unfairly judgemental. But on this occasion, so too was Sandra. Because it was just impossible not to feel that this market was 'worn out', a place full of people who were acquainted with only poverty and anxiety and who were resigned to no improvement in their condition – ever. They were certainly unlike their counterparts in the 'traditional' parts of this country, not only in their reluctance to smile but also in their apparent reluctance even to recognise a potential punter. There was no hard sell in this emporium and barely even a hard stare – but just ubiquitous indifference. It was… well, quite depressing – as well as being uncomfortably hot – and consequently at least two of the privileged visitors to this place were more relieved than ever to be back on their air-conditioned conveyance, even if it meant another stint in the company of near-stationary traffic with very little prospect of ever finding a nice little pub…

It took quite some time to reach the exit from the market car park where it met Honiara's main thoroughfare, and during this period the on-board local guide entertained his charges by enlightening them on the nation's plans to encourage the growth of tourism in the Solomon Islands. He maintained that there were significant opportunities in Honiara itself – ignoring its threadbare state and its desperate lack of infrastructure. That was understandable, thought Brian. Why indeed shouldn't this enthusiastic young man be enthusiastic about the prospects for his country and for himself? But then he went on to explain that the status of Guadalcanal as a battlefield in WWII attracted a constant stream of Americans to this island – and Honiara – and that in only a few days' time an American cruise ship would be arriving to decant not just eighty or so people but two and a half thousand people! That would mean, thought Brian, that these visitors would need not just four minibuses but instead every bus on the island (all equipped for overnight accommodation), a rapidly constructed road system in and around Honiara, copious amounts of patience and a daunting amount of heavy-duty fortitude. Without this combination of essentials they would be unable to endure their visit to this city and would stand no chance at all of completing it before WWIII broke out. This guide, Brian concluded, was either a prize-winning optimist or a professional comedian.

Well, it looked as though it was the latter. Because after assuring his bus-full of passengers that this gargantuan ship really would be decanting those hordes of Americans in just a few days' time, he then announced that the police car at the exit from the car park was there to provide the minibus convoy with an escort. Everybody laughed, and it wasn't until the police car turned on its siren and began to carve a path through the stationary traffic – for the benefit of just the four minibuses – that the smirks and grins finally disappeared. He hadn't been joking. It seemed that so infrequent were cruise ship visits to this city that the city was prepared to help out as required and at least to facilitate the movement of its honoured guests through its clogged arteries. Brian was impressed, and so were his fellow passengers. They were all being given the VIP treatment – for no good reason. Although, there again, thought Brian, maybe the police had been told that these visitors were on their way to the National Parliament, and that induced in them a reflex response, something along the lines of 'carve a pathway through the plebs for the masters'…

He ticked himself off yet again. The police were just being courteous, and the buses weren't even going directly to the National Parliament. Free of the clogged arteries, they first meandered through the Chinese quarter (which could more accurately have been described as the nondescript quarter) and then they ventured up into some rather scruffy suburbs which afforded them good views of the surrounding countryside and of people cleaning cars. Only then did they make their way to this country's seat of government, which, according to the on-board guide, had been built with American aid in honour of all the American soldiers and marines who had lost their lives on Guadalcanal in the Second World War. And oddly enough the actual build had been undertaken by contractors from... Japan.

Well, the first thing that Brian noticed when the buses pulled into a parking lot to the side of the National Parliament building was that the Japanese had used a lot of concrete in its construction. The second thing he noticed was that the concrete had been employed in realising a design that might be described as either audacious or atrocious, depending on one's perspective or possibly on one's eyesight. It wasn't very big, but it was concrete-bunker-like at its base with, above this base, a sort of concrete conical 'hat'. The overall effect was... interesting. So much so that if Brian had been shown a photo of it out of context and had been asked to decide whether it was a) the home of the Social Sciences department at Keele University, b) the now demolished Basingstoke Central Library or c) the Houses of Parliament for the Solomon Islands, he would have opted for Keele, Basingstoke and Honiara in that order. It seemed to have little to associate it with any Solomon Islands' tradition but more to do with a combination of self-indulgent architecture and an over-indulgence in concrete. And maybe there was a hint of hubris in there as well.

Anyway, it was in use. There were, apparently, legislators in this edifice – legislating – and consequently the visiting VIPs had to restrict their visit to this national assembly to an inspection of its exterior and a rather more interesting inspection of Honiara below it. Because the National Parliament building's best feature by far was its position: on a pronounced high point overlooking the capital and the Pacific Ocean beyond. From here the city looked almost impressive and none of its fading fabric was visible without the use of a spyglass. And doesn't everywhere, thought Brian, look that much better not only from afar, but also under a tropical, unbroken blue sky. If only, he also thought, Basingstoke was located in the South Pacific…

And if only that police escort had hung around. But it hadn't. Which meant that the return journey to the *Caledonian Sky* was about as rapid as a bill passing through parliament – whether through the parliament they'd just left or through any other parliament on Earth. Such are the workings of modern democracy, which shouldn't ever, of course, be confused with the workings of a sustainable democracy. But more of that later, because Brian and Sandra and their fellow travellers had now been delivered back to their floating oasis, and it was time to freshen up and prepare oneself for lunch – and for an exercise in how to avoid disparaging comments about a capital city that one has just visited and a capital city with which one has just been comprehensively underwhelmed.

Brian managed it, but not without resorting to a discussion of noses and nostrils, and his theory that at some time in the past they had been known as snoses and snostrils…

It was all garbage, but he had never been able to discover why so many nose-related words began with the letters 'sn'. And there were lots of them – as he explained to his four unfortunate table companions this lunchtime – and as Sandra had heard explained many times before. They included the words 'snout', 'snore', 'snuff', 'snorkel', 'sniff', 'snot', 'snort', 'snuffle', 'sneeze', 'snivel' and 'snoop' – as in poking one's nose in. Or should that be, he suggested, 'poking one's snose in'? Because it did seem peculiar that the organ at the centre of this 'sn' mania – and the two holes at its base – were now missing out on a combination of those two essential letters and had to make do with just one of them at their outset. There had been an etymological wrongdoing, Brian proposed, with a person or persons unknown making off with an 's' and so leaving the two principals in the 'sn' band of brothers naked but for their 'n's, and wasn't it about time something was done about this? Wasn't it about time that he – and maybe the members of his bemused audience this lunchtime – went off and began the process of restitution by referring only to 'snoses' and 'snostrils' and correcting all those they met who insisted on still employing the depleted and indeed denuded words of 'noses' and 'nostrils'?

It may have been better simply to have been disparaging about Honiara, but the damage had been done, and it was left to Sandra to clear up the pieces by suggesting to Brian that they skipped coffee and left their table companions to finish their meal at their leisure.

And in any event, these table companions had indicated that they would be opting for this afternoon's further on-shore excursion, and both Brian and Sandra were keen not to be drawn into another encounter with Honiara or its hinterland, which they might be if they remained at the table. They had no wish to visit war memorials or battle sites – which was the advertised purpose of the afternoon outing – in part because these monuments and locations related to a conflict with which they had no connection and in part because they had now experienced the local traffic conditions and the local weather conditions (it was still remarkably hot). Oh, and in part because Sandra wanted a rest and Brian wanted to indulge himself in another bout of melancholia before getting on to some more serious limerick writing. And one could do none of these things while snarled up in a Honiara traffic jam or while contemplating the futility of war – as one would no doubt be doing in any tour of memorials and battle sites.

So, Brian and Sandra were soon back in their cabin, and when Sandra's admonishment of her husband had been completed, she first attended to some domestic admin and he first attended to an inspection of Honiara's port operations. He did this from a chair on the cabin's balcony, and he soon became fascinated by the nature of these operations – which involved landing craft and towed barges...

It seemed that the *Caledonian Sky* was the only seagoing vessel that was making use of the city's dock. Indeed, it may have been occupying the only dockside mooring. This undoubtedly cost the ship's operators quite a lot of money, which was probably why most vessels visiting Honiara eschewed any actual contact with a quayside and instead moored well out to sea and then relied on local tenders or towed barges to transfer their cargo to shore. It spoke again of a lack of development and a dearth of wealth in this country and of how even its principal city was no more than 'just getting by'. Brian found it all really quite dispiriting, and he was therefore ideally primed for his next descent into the realms of desolation. Indeed, the sight of all that 'make do and mend' out there even provided him with his theme for this afternoon's bout of misery, and this theme was 'progress' – or, more accurately, 'the illusion of progress'.

It started with his reminding himself that he had let himself fall into the trap of regarding a lack of physical facilities here in Honiara as a lack of 'progress', as a failure in that relentless march forward by mankind in order to sustain its theme of 'continuous improvement'. In other words, here – apparently – was a conspicuous example of humanity stumbling in its plans for its development into the future, for its programme of indefinite and continuous betterment – all encompassed within that one magic word: 'progress'. Well, the point he further reminded himself of was that all this 'progress' is a myth, and this is because there hasn't actually been any in the past and there never will be any in the future.

He was well aware that this somewhat negative view of progress was shared by nobody he knew – other than Sandra – and if he admitted that he held it himself he would open himself up to ridicule or worse. However, that didn't mean he was wrong. It simply meant that humanity in general was confusing 'progress' with the impact of a series of 'useful innovations', that is to say, the impact of a series of discoveries and inventions that have greatly eased the burden of living for at least some of its members. But this is in no way genuine advancement. How can it be when humanity's history is a long procession of conflicts, abuses, failures and disasters and continues to be so – and all its institutions and administrations are riddled with as much corruption now as they have always been? And with this reality of human existence staring it in the face, how can humanity think that the future will be in any way better than the past or the present? How can it fool itself into thinking that it will in some way make 'further progress' having made none whatsoever so far?

The truth of the matter, in Brian's opinion, was that no species on this planet 'makes progress'. Tigers don't. Worms don't. Flounders don't. Instead they either survive as a species or they do not survive as a species. And it's just the same for us. Because no matter how clever we believe we are and no matter how many discoveries we've made and how many inventions we've devised, we are still just a species, just a particularly smart-arsed animal that's been around for a brief spell of Earth-time and that may not be around for a great deal longer. After all, not only is mankind not progressing, but what it is wrongly interpreting as progress is actually a real threat to its survival – and an imminent threat at that.

'Progress' is enabling more and more humans to live on this globe, and even to stack themselves up in places like Hong Kong. Well, the only real advancement involved here is the sort that takes a species towards a cliff edge and then over it. Because this 'progress' is also allowing us to travel further and faster, and in doing so, screw up more of the world at an ever-increasing rate. It is allowing us to become more efficient – in clearing the oceans of fish, the savannah of animals and whole tracts of the world of their beauty as, with 'advanced' techniques and equipment, we plough them up, reduce them to green deserts or cover them in concrete (whether in the shape of national parliaments or not).

Brian paused in his thinking here, because he was only too conscious that when trying out this theory on his friends in the past, not one of them had accepted it. However, a few of them had wobbled a bit when he had reduced his argument to their personal circumstances. Yes, when he'd invited then to consider the 'progress' they'd witnessed over their own lifetime, they weren't quite so sure. They had, for example, seen how their children were having to make do with smaller houses than they had. They were only too aware of how the roads they used had become more and more congested. And they also recognised that public services appeared to be going backwards, whilst at the same time there was more interference in their own lives than ever before – and more conformity demanded of them than ever before. Together, all these features, they might just concede, did not add up to 'progress'.

Well, with his friends now gently wobbling, Brian would then ask them to look a little further afield – at the world – and he'd ask them to consider whether they believed that the pollution of the oceans could be construed as some sort of progress. Or how about the decimation of the African elephant – or the increasing lunacy in the Middle East, or the exodus of people from Africa and Asia into Europe or, indeed, that little thing called global warming?

This is when he generally encountered 'overload'. This is when they began to feel oppressed (Brian liked to think by the weight of logic and irrefutable evidence) and wanted to revert to the myth of human progress. After all, look at all that GM stuff and solar panels…

Yes, Brian knew he and Sandra were on their own on this one – and that the belief in human progress was fundamental to people's ability to make sense of their lives. After all, if one takes away progress, then one takes away purpose. One reveals the future for what it really is: just a repeat of the past but with more apps and more city breaks in Europe. Until, that is, the future hits the buffers; until that time when the penny drops and mankind not only realises that it cannot progress but also that it can only survive or become extinct. And at the current pace of 'progress' that point in time will soon be reached – along with the realisation by the whole of humanity that the smart money is on extinction.

Oh dear. Brian had started off with what could be interpreted as no more than an exercise in semantics and had ended up predicting the demise of the human race. And heck, even though that would inevitably have a silver lining, it was still all rather depressing and he now felt absolutely inundated by melancholia. Contemplating the end of one's species was bad enough, but regarding oneself as having contributed to this end – through an assault on the concept of progress – was even worse. He was now in a particularly bad place and needed to do something about it. So he did. First by picking up his pen and writing some more limericks and then later by bombarding his dinner companions with his views on how one went about fashioning a system of sustainable democracy out of the current mess of modern democracy...

His targets at the table were the famous four – Thor, Lise, Paul and Lydia – and the first salvo of his bombardment was a brief explanation of why modern Western democracies are all holed below the waterline and destined to sink. He could have made this salvo last an hour or so, but he restricted himself to the principal problem with modern democracies, which was of course the way all political parties go about getting their candidates elected. Forget ideals and visions and what needs to be done for the future and just shower the electorate with lots of promises. That's all that most of this electorate want to hear. And they certainly don't want to hear how all those promises are going to be paid for, nor that the promises have now grown to such a ridiculous level that they cannot be funded out of tax, and accordingly most governments in the West now routinely borrow money to make up the shortfall. Indeed borrowing has become an integral part of the way a democratic country's affairs are run, and governments can even get into trouble if they are not seen to be exploiting low interest rates by borrowing even more. Well, Brian concluded, there might be a parallel universe somewhere in which money borrowed does not have to be paid back, but in the one we're stuck with, it does. There will come a day when the creditors want their money and they cannot get it, at which point it will become apparent how our current form of democracy is a fraud and how it has been hollowed out from within by this practice of making reckless promises to an electorate that cannot legitimately be met. Hence the need to fashion a new form of democracy before the present one caves in.

Well, nobody had left the table yet, and Sandra hadn't called a halt to his campaign. So Brian proceeded to fire off three more rapid-fire salvoes to press home his apparent advantage. They were in the form of the radical changes that needed to be made to the present arrangements in order to deliver truly sustainable democracies.

Rapid-fire salvo one was a call to raise the voting age to thirty-five. Nobody below twenty-five, he proposed, should be doing anything other than exploring his or her sexuality and behaving irresponsibly. They should definitely not be concerning themselves with politics. Those between twenty-five and thirty-five might legitimately be developing an interest in politics, but only by their mid-30s will they stand any real chance of properly knowing their minds or of understanding enough of national affairs to enable them to make any rational political judgements.

Rapid-fire salvo two was the institution of a licensing system – on the basis that if one needs a licence to drive a car, own a shotgun or watch a telly, then one certainly needs a licence to vote. Step forward all those 35-year-olds who want to be enfranchised and invite them to apply for said licence – which will be granted only after they have passed a 'fit to vote' exam. This will not be a particularly draconian exercise but it will require them to demonstrate that they understand the basics of government and that they are au fait with other little issues like who the current prime minister is and what a general election is for. Clearly a large proportion of 35-year-olds will not even step forward to apply for this licence – and their absence from the democratic process will be no great loss.

Rapid-fire salvo three – and the salvo that was the most potentially devastating. And this was because it involved Brian explaining how, with this new mature and knowledgeable electorate, there was one further step to take, and this entailed ditching that sacrosanct one-man-one-vote principle. In its place each voter would have anywhere between ten votes and just one vote, depending on his or her circumstances. So if he (or she) was a taxpayer who had consistently paid but never received, then he or she would have ten votes. A taxpayer who, say, was in receipt of child benefits, would have just nine votes. And this attrition of voting power would go all the way down to a non-taxpaying serial recipient of state funds who would have just a single vote.

Here Brian paused for breath – and to gauge how his bombardment had been received. Possibly not very well, he thought. But that wasn't about to stop him using his artillery one last time – to summarise what his changes would result in. And this was the cessation of unrealistic promises by politicians – because the voting power would now lie in the hands of people who were not only genuinely interested in politics but who were also the very people who would have to pay for these promises. Furthermore, if his remedy and its intended outcome were regarded as in any way controversial then they were no more controversial, he argued, than the misguided idea of hanging on to a ship that has a large hole below the waterline and that will inevitably sink into a sea of fascism or something even worse.

Thor agreed! But he then made the observation that he could be just as whimsical as Brian if he chose to – although he might lose out when it came to moralising. So Brian had been sussed, and not just by Thor. From further comments around the table, it became apparent that they all now knew him far too well, and as soon as he'd embarked on his campaign to rehabilitate democracy they had all suspected that he wasn't being entirely serious. Well, not entirely...

Anyway, the rest of the meal passed off without any further bombardments and in due course Brian and Sandra were back in their room, and Brian was into recitation mode. His limericks this evening were as follows:

There was a young girl from Seattle
Who developed a serious rattle
Some said it would halt
With a man in her vault
But I think that was just tittle-tattle

And

There was a young girl with big eyes
And with boobs of a similar size
Like eggs cut in half
They made people laugh
So she christened them Morecambe and Wise

And

There was a young girl from Australia
Who, with boys, was an absolute failure
Although she looked great
She could not get a date
Coz the poor girl was named Jenny Talia

Now, at this point, Sandra interrupted to complain that there were far too many young girls tonight and that they were all being horribly abused, especially the poor woman with the small boobs. Brian took this criticism on board and immediately switched to young men, his store of completed limericks enabling him to finish with:

There was a young man from Hong Kong
Who was blessed with a sizeable schlong
So he took the full blame
For the fallout that came
When he housed it in just a small thong

And

There was a young man who was found
On a golf course, laid out on the ground
He'd been hit on the head
By the woman he'd wed
When she found he'd been playing a round

Sandra, at this conclusion to the proceedings, acknowledged Brian's change of gender in his limericks but then checked with her husband whether he was eligible to vote…

Brian said he was but that he regretted having only one vote. He wanted ten. Of course.

*I*t was the day of the limericks competition. So Brian had woken up thinking about… President Chump.

Well, not so much about the president himself, but about the people with whom he'd surrounded himself, that motley collection of family and friends whose competency for office appeared to be based either on their close relationship with El Presidente or on their close relationship with oodles of dosh. Yes, you could qualify for his inner circle by your being in his immediate family or, if not related to him, by your having been a successful warrior in the fields of banking, investment management, hedge fund manipulation or some other such scam, where you would have already come away with the odd few billion as well as a healthy disdain for your fellow man. Such were the people who, with Donald J, were going to make America great again – and possibly themselves even greater. And then there was how they all looked…

It could not be a coincidence that they all looked like replicants, like those flawless androids that featured in *Blade Runner.* And they certainly did. The men looked like polished copies of gangsters, facsimiles of hoodlums from the twenties and thirties whose idea of a good hairstyle entailed so much grease that, without a single exception, their shampoo of choice was industrial-strength Swarfega. And they apparently didn't own a comb between them, but instead they had all equipped themselves with their own personal Dolce & Gabbana mini-rakes, with which they could plough the furrows through their generously lubricated locks to create that authentic mobster look that was so much in demand in the White House today. And then there were the women...

They were the classic replicants, perfect copies of... perfect impossibilities, (allegedly) females of the species who were alien to the species and more reminiscent of lacquered reproductions than they were of real people. And really, how else could one regard specimens of the gentle gender who were even more unblemished than they were unabashed by their positions? No way would there ever be a hair out of place, a flaw in their make-up, a crease in their skirt, or a distressing panty line on show – or indeed anything that defines the rest of us as fallible, imperfect, genuine humans and not as something that has been produced in an intricate mould and then been buffed up and burnished ever since.

Yes, Brian had been watching too many of those American news programmes on the telly – when he should have been immersing himself either in the passage of the *Caledonian Sky* through Melanesia or, more urgently, in the finalisation of a number of prize-winning limericks. After all, the deadline for submissions for today's limerick competition was noon and, as there was another excursion to undertake before then, that meant that he had no more than an hour to tidy up his efforts and decide which of his limerick wonders to submit. No point, he thought, in diluting his chances by presenting the judges with an overload of odes, and much better to tender the cream of the crop, maybe just three limericks which would seal his victory in what might be quite a tough tournament. There again... if he didn't partake of this morning's visit ashore, he would, of course, have rather more than an hour to sort things out. And that might not be a bad idea.

It was his back again. It was already more than uncomfortable. And it really wasn't an excuse back but more an authentic, 'bugger me' back, the sort of back that he knew would probably let him down big-time if he asked anything of it other than maybe some sedentary limerick sorting. It certainly wouldn't take well to being asked to make its way around another village. And that was what was on offer this morning: an inspection of yet another manifestation of Melanesian life, this one contained in a place called Telina. This was a small settlement located on one of the many islands scattered throughout a large saltwater bay called Marovo Lagoon, which itself was situated in the New Georgia Islands, a group of islands at the north-west end of the Solomon chain and next door to Papua New Guinea. So, the questions were: a) should he duck out of this last chance to see a little more of a country he would probably never visit again – and so save his back – and, more importantly, b) what would be Sandra's reaction to her being abandoned yet again?

Well, he decided only after breakfast what the answer to a) was. He would indeed take the road to 'wimpdom' and spend the morning with his limericks while nursing his back. When he announced this to Sandra he then learnt what the answer to b) was, not so much in her use of words but more in the volume she adopted when she responded to the announcement. She clearly wasn't very happy. Indeed, she was so unhappy that she inadvertently provided Brian with a few very choice terms that he would subsequently use in the composition of a couple of regular as opposed to competition limericks. For which he was very grateful. Albeit he did not make this gratitude known. It wouldn't, he decided, be the best way to turn down the volume…

Ultimately, Sandra accepted her fate and went off to attach herself to Thor and Lise for the trip ashore, leaving her hopeless husband alone in his 'cell'. Here he would spend the next three hours on his limerick agenda, or at least nearly three hours – just as soon as he'd extracted himself from his next bout of melancholia…

It was that damned back again. It wasn't just causing him physical pain but also mental pain. It was reminding him one more time of the fact that he was getting old and he could do nothing about it. He couldn't even anguish about it properly – because he'd already done that earlier on this voyage when he'd absolutely wallowed in the unavoidable consequences of the unavoidable ageing process. But… he hadn't wallowed in how getting on in years could also make you begin to believe that you were becoming ever more obsolete. How life was changing around you all the time – and you weren't. You were locked into a time more than forty years ago, a time when you felt relatively comfortable with the world. And a time when you didn't have to witness every day the sorts of sights and the sorts of attitudes that then would have been regarded as either alien or simply reprehensible.

For example, Brian still walked down a street with both of his hands unencumbered. Should a tenner be blown past or a baby be dropped from a fourth-floor window, he stood a good chance of catching either – even if the latter would inevitably play havoc with his back. But all those around him could do no such thing. By the time they'd dealt with their smartphones and relieved themselves of either their water bottles or their skinny lattes, the note would be down the street and the baby would be on the pavement. And anyway, they'd all be more concerned with filming the incident rather than engaging with it, anything to provide a little bit of material for their Facebook page – particularly as they hadn't had a new tattoo for weeks, and they couldn't really keep posting pictures of their old ones.

And that was another aspect of obsolescence: the belief that one's skin didn't necessarily make an ideal canvas, and that dressing it in an ever-increasing number of tacky or extremely silly tattoos was not just mindless but also aesthetically very disturbing. Even tattoos on slender young bodies were pretty revolting, but on the more pneumatic members of the public they were simply hideous, and as their owners began to age and all those sags and wrinkles began to overtake the smooth, Brian wondered how they'd cope. How they would deal with that lion on their right arm that now looked like a walrus, and how they would regard that angel of death on their right calf now it was shot through with varicose veins.

It went on and on. Women with a quite incredible misunderstanding of clothes sizes, a failure in their thinking that often manifested itself in their choice of their trousers and leggings. Then there were men and women who, having chosen to live without a dining table in their homes, now conducted their dining whilst walking down the street. And men and women, infected with a disturbing strain of narcissism, capturing yet another selfie image of themselves to join the thousands more that already bore witness to their sad self-obsession. And if one was incautious enough to switch on the telly… any number of shameless tossers parading their quite repulsive behaviour, their incredible immaturity, their stunning level of ignorance – and rather too much of their tattooed bodies – in the name of 'reality show' entertainment. In fact, Brian had learnt to accommodate much of the vulgarity and stupidity on display in the street, but was now convinced he would be turned to stone (not euphemistically) if he ever, by accident, caught sight of even a few seconds of something like *Celebrity Big Brother* or *The Only Way is Essex.* The behaviour on show in these sorts of offerings didn't just make him feel obsolete; it also made him feel quite embarrassed. After all, wasn't he of the same species as their protagonists, even if not that similar in appearance? Neither, for that matter, did he have similar attitudes.

This was what really underlined his obsolescence: attitudes that were now commonplace but that when he was twenty-one would have been regarded as perverse if not bizarre. And at the head of this cavalcade of 'modern-day mind-sets' was the belief that one's emotions were no longer one's private property and something to be shared with only one's close friends and confidants, but instead that they were to be broadcast to the widest audience possible. So that in the same way that one was now able to empathise and 'identify' with the trending sufferings of somebody one has never met (and never knew about until one had logged in this morning) it is now possible to share one's sorrow at the loss of one's pet iguana with countless other... people – if, of course, one has the necessary profile and the necessary misunderstanding of what real emotions are all about.

Then, just behind this 'emotional indiscretion' comes the rest of the procession, a cortege of other indigestible modern beliefs, too numerous to count, but including such horrors as a complete lack of self-responsibility and a conviction that every mishap in life is somebody else's fault – and generally worth claiming for. Then there is the 'righteousness syndrome', very common among the more educated in society, which can manifest itself in many forms including the propensity to take offence (often on somebody else's behalf) where no offence was intended, the desire to measure the past in terms of today's values and therefore to designate any historical figure as a racist or a beast, and the tendency to sit in judgement on all those contemporary figures who don't share one's misguided, soppy, naïve and ultimately dangerous views. Oh, and let's not forget all those other dreadful attitudes that have arrived with a resurgence of religion in this country, which go way beyond the perverse and bizarre and into a territory we might just label as 'eventually apocalyptic'.

Oh dear, Brian hadn't meant to go down this road this morning, and he finally decided enough was enough. He managed this by reminding himself that most people, if not all people, absorb a series of attitudes when they are about twenty-one, which they then use to calibrate their own and other people's behaviour for the rest of their lives. Consequently, as general attitudes change – as they do – these slowly ageing people become further and further removed from their own benchmark attitudes, and their sense that they are becoming increasingly obsolete inevitably flourishes, helped to no small degree by all those unsettling sights on the street and on the telly. And so wasn't it about time that he arrested his gloom and accepted the fact that becoming out of date was just a natural consequence of living past twenty-one – and rather than being gloomy he should just be very happy that he'd got so far past that milestone age? Which wasn't the best fix of his recurrent melancholia, but it did do the job, and he was soon properly immersed in a whole clutch of dodgy and not quite so dodgy limericks.

He was still immersed in them when Sandra returned, at which point he thought it politic to set his odes to one side and enquire about the success or otherwise of her expedition.

Well, she lost no time at all in telling him that he had been a fool not to join her.

The Zodiac ride itself had been fascinating, as a whole convoy of these vessels had made their way through the

202

reefs of the lagoon, and had then been greeted by a war canoe. When Brian looked puzzled at this revelation she then went on to explain that it wasn't actually the canoe that had done the greeting but the dozen or so warriors aboard it, all of whom were daubed with white warpaint and all of whom were converts to the school of howling and shouting as an acceptable form of greeting – and had probably been enjoying themselves more than they had been fretting about their obsolescence. And they were obsolete. Or at least their behaviour was. Because it stemmed from a time when not all the communities in the Marovo Lagoon were signed up to a peaceful coexistence convention. No. Instead they were very often at each other's throats and quite often, literally.

Anyway, the Zodiacs eventually delivered their passengers to Telina Village where, depending on one's perspective, more obsolescence or more tradition was on show. This first took the form of a performance of some intricate, long-established dances – by both men and women – dressed in some long-established costumes. And then there was some traditional but at the same time ageless activity in the form of retail therapy. There were no designer clothes and no T-shirts on offer, of course, but instead an attractive display of very skilfully carved wooden artefacts, a product, no doubt, of keeping alive what might otherwise have become an obsolete expertise.

Sandra hadn't bought anything and had removed herself from temptation by joining a short walk into the local forest. There were orchids to see – and a forest to smell – and that had trumped any amount of even the most enticing display of merchandise. When Sandra told him this, Brian, not for the first time, was very relieved that he had not set up camp with an incurable shopaholic. Otherwise he might now be contemplating how to get back to Blighty an apparently splendid carving of a Solomons' fish eagle killing an octopus. Which was bound to have sticky-out bits as well as being inescapably large. Though not necessarily obsolete…

In the meantime, however, he had something else to contemplate. It was coming up to noon, which meant that he had finally to settle on which three limericks he would submit for the limerick competition – and then get himself off to reception and submit them.

It was done, and then it was time for lunch. This passed off without any mention of obsolescence at Brian's table but with one or two twinges in his back. This wasn't good news. The afternoon entertainment was to take the form of a final mass-snorkel in the Marovo Lagoon, a lagoon that was primarily known for its snorkelling opportunities and that was so full of fish that many snorkellers had likened it to swimming in a massive bowl of (whole) fish soup.

Well, Brian would have to take their word for it. He would have to report for sick parade again, albeit on this occasion his wife would be there to keep him company. The arrival of rain, together with the promise of some deep-water snorkelling where the outer wall of the lagoon's double reef dropped to 250 metres in depth, extinguished any desire on her part to take to the water. Instead, from their cabin balcony, she would take in the view of all those brave souls who did don their snorkels and, at the same time, she would try to ignore the fact that Brian was still fiddling away in limerick-land. He was either constructing some more of his heavy-duty stuff or he was brooding about his competition entries. It was impossible to tell, and anyway she didn't want to know. No more than she wanted to be out in that lagoon. It was now pouring down out there and most of the tree-fringed islands that formed a backdrop to the snorkelling party were no longer visible. And Ingrid, the snorkel master, was just visible in her Zodiac, holding an umbrella over her head. She was clearly soaked and would be in need of the restorative power of a bathroom, complete with hairdryer, before she was ready for the Farewell Cocktails and the captain's Farewell Dinner, which were the promised diversions for this coming evening. Oh, and it would be during the Farewell Cocktails that the limerick competition would be held...

Brian, as far as possible, had prepared himself for this ordeal, both mentally and physically (he had put on a jacket). And he now sat with Sandra, Thor, Lise, Paul and Lydia in the Caledonian Lounge, nursing a gin and tonic and a wish that he hadn't participated in this damned competition in the first place. It was one thing to have one's limericks judged by one's wife; it was quite another to have them judged by 'the public', especially when you would be sharing the company of this same public for the next couple of days. Anyway, there was nothing he could do now but wait and see what would happen – and how it would happen.

Well, proceedings commenced with the announcement by Ian, Garth's principal historian (and

205

on-board fount of knowledge on all things to do with Captain Cook), that a host of limerick submissions had been whittled down to just ten, and that these ten were now about to be whittled down to one… This would be done on the basis of popular appeal. That is to say that the congregation in the lounge would decide which of the ten selected entries was the winner – after all ten of them had been read out by their authors!

Crikey, thought Brian. This was turning into a nightmare. Although, there again, maybe his efforts weren't in the top ten. Maybe he'd flunked it completely. But no. Because Ian's first limerick revelation was that one worthwhile effort, although it had correctly dealt with a valid aspect of the Pacific Ocean – namely the land divers of Pentecost Island – had fallen foul of the 'no political content' rule. And although it was therefore not eligible to be allowed into the final, it could still be read out for the amusement of all. 'So would… Brian please come up and read it for us?'

Gulp! And then another gulp – of gin and tonic – and Brian was on his feet and being presented with his ode to recite to the crowd. Before he could even think about his situation he was off, and the first limerick of the evening was revealed to be as follows:

Those brave young men would bungee jump
And risk a painful jarring thump
In fact it's said
If to the head
They could end up like Donald Trump

Laughter and applause! Amazing, thought Brian. And then he thought that was it. He could now sink back into his old-people's chair and just participate as a member of the audience. And this is what he did for the next five (passable) entries. Until it was number six – which turned out to be the second of his three entries!

Well, this time he was up like a shot and after a theatrical throat-clearing was into recital mode without a pause. This time his limerick was:

There was a girl from Melanesia
Who free of charge would seek to tease yer
For one and four
She'd do much more
For half a crown she'd really please yer

This time there was more laughter than ever (the audience having, by this time, dispensed with applause in favour of a vocal sign of appreciation). Brian was quite excited. His was the only limerick so far to include the word 'Melanesia' and he knew that references to (yes) an obsolete currency and to implied sex acts would go down pretty well with his… mature audience. The trouble was that the next offering – from a guy whom Brian did not know but who seemed to station himself at the lounge bar whenever possible – went down even better. The whole gathering simply loved it. It had to be the winner.

However, there were still three more limericks to go. The first of these was recited by another man who was completely unknown to Brian, but whom Brian immediately took a shine to – because his effort was just that, an attempt rather than a worthwhile limerick, and no way was it a winner.

Now there were just two limericks left, at which point Ian appeared to change the whole structure of the competition by announcing that the winning entry would be whichever of this remaining pair (which he and his teammates had chosen before the recitation stage (?)) mustered the greater applause. Oh, and the authors of these two limericks were the guy from the bar and Brian – with Brian to go first…

Shit! This wasn't what Brian was expecting, but he didn't hesitate to get to his feet yet again, and what had to be his killer limerick was soon being deployed. It was:

There was a young chappie from Tonga
Who was known for the length of his donger
At rest it was more
Than two foot and four
En garde it was half a yard longer

Well, the crowd went crazy. Brian was overcome. Right up until the bar fly read out his limerick and the crowd went very slightly crazier. At least that's what was claimed. And not only was this other guy's applause not actually louder than his own at all, but his limerick – in Brian's opinion – was simply not as good. Which made the whole thing an outrage and the result a real travesty, causing Brian to mobilise his best 'good loser' disposition while, at the same time, fuming within.

However, his friends were quick to offer their

condolences, and anyway, he told himself, it was just a silly contest, and he had, after all, achieved a second place in it. Furthermore, there was now a Farewell Dinner to enjoy and therefore the facility to get himself ratted if he really wanted to.

In the event, he remained relatively sober. He and Sandra had found themselves on a table with four people with whom they had shared a meal before and a new couple with whom they had only exchanged a few words. It proved interesting company, if not always for the right reasons. So, for example, when one of the known quartet embarked on a diatribe about the correct pronunciation of Latin, everybody around the table was captivated, if at the same time a little puzzled. Like Brian and Sandra they probably recalled from their Latin studies at school that there were no ancient Romans still around who could have settled the matter one way or another. And, as everybody knew, audio recordings during the time of the Roman Empire were only in their infancy and consequently were of very poor quality…

Just as captivating but less puzzling was a discussion with the two 'unknowns' at the table – a couple who answered to the names of Anton and Meg – initiated by a casual reference to the music of Neil Innes. This developed into a full-blown encomium on Mr Innes, with contributions from Brian, Sandra, Anton and Meg, who, it transpired, were all of the opinion that this man of music is one of the most talented but most underrated musicians/composers of the modern age. Indeed, it was soon agreed that, had he wanted to, he could probably have come up with a much better limerick than the effort that had just won – and then put it to music to make it even better. If only he'd been on this cruise. And if only he could have constituted a full stop to today's overindulgence in odes of five lines. But he wasn't on this cruise and he could do nothing about Brian assaulting Sandra with more bloody limericks when they were back in their cabin. Tonight, partly to get the taste of that loss out of his mouth, Brian would serve up no less than six!

These were:

There was a young woman called Trump
Who boasted a well-rounded rump
But this rump, I declare
Was just down to some air
And the use of a pneumatic pump

Here, Sandra interrupted her husband – to inform him that he had to withdraw this one because it was overtly political. Brian acknowledged this comment, but then continued. His next was as follows:

There was a young girl from Chicago
Whose boobs could be classed as bulk cargo
So huge was this pair
That when travelling by air
She'd have them sent on by Wells Fargo

And then

There was a young girl called Simone
Who learnt a new use for her phone
It was really good fun
But in more ways than one
It did rather bring down the tone

And then

There was a young girl called Atari
Who married a young, rich Qatari
It has to be said
He was piss-poor in bed
But he did own a big red Ferrari

And then

There was a young woman from Deal
Who herself she would quite often feel
She quite liked her tum
And she did love her bum
But her top spot was always her keel

And finally – thankfully

There was a young girl who would laugh
At a miner she thought was real daft
But the laughs had to go
When she looked down below
And saw the huge size of his shaft

That was it. Even Brian was now limericked out. And

Sandra… well, even before her husband had embarked on this evening session, she had wished that limericks had long ago been declared 'totally obsolete' and consequently were no longer in (perpetual) circulation…

15.

*B*rian's first thought on waking up was whether it would be possible to arrange a rematch. After all, boxers did. For them it was almost a matter of course. Get knocked out in a title match, and then sort out another opportunity to be knocked out again – or maybe, on that next occasion, to win.

Well, it sounded a plausible enough idea in those first few seconds of consciousness, but then, as Brian moved his mind into gear, some rather more rational thinking came into play. Boxing and competitive limerick writing, he reminded himself, are two very different disciplines with very little in common – other than the possibility of losing twice in quick succession to the same opponent. Yes, how would he react to being beaten again by last night's winner? Once was bad enough. Oh, and of course there was the minor matter of not having any new limericks to field. After all, he could not imagine for a minute that Sandra would allow him to use any of the tasteless compositions he'd assembled on this voyage and which were definitely not designed for public consumption. At least not for that slice of public that gathered in the Caledonian Lounge every evening.

And that meant he would just have to learn to live with his defeat of the previous evening and possibly distract himself with other matters. Like, for example, the Solomon Sea.

Today the *Caledonian Sky* would be steaming towards its next destination: the port of Rabaul in Papua New Guinea. This place was 471 nautical miles from the ship's starting point of Marovo Lagoon and therefore it would not be reached until tomorrow. That is to say that the ship's passengers were in for another 'day at sea', and the sea that would feature in this particular day at sea was, not surprisingly, the Solomon Sea. This is the huge expanse of water, with an area of 280,000 square miles, bounded on the west by New Guinea, on the north by New Britain and on the east by the Solomon Islands. Brian wasn't able to spot it himself, but the seafloor of this vast chunk of the Pacific Ocean is divided into two principal basins. Or at least that's what a fact sheet he'd been given asserted anyway. And this same fact sheet then went on to state that the 'New Britain Basin' to the north has a general depth of 13,000 feet, with a few deeper areas, including the 'New Britain Trench' plunging to a maximum depth of 29,988 feet!

That, Brian decided, was bloody deep. It meant that it was quite possible that at some time today – if the *Caledonian Sky* actually crossed that trench – there would be a column of water below him that was even taller than Everest (the height of that popular selfie destination being a mere 29,029 feet). Looked at another way, 5,998 Ronnie Corbetts could be stacked upright in that trench, one on top of another, and only the top Ronnie Corbett would be able to breathe. In Brian's mind, this was such a startling illustration of the incredible depth of the New Britain Trench, that he reported it to Sandra. Her immediate response was to question the availability of so many Ronnie Corbetts, but also to point out, after a little exercise in mental arithmetic, that the pressure at the bottom of the trench would be approaching six tons per square inch. This she maintained would compress a large number of the lower Ronnie Corbetts into little more than Corbett pancakes, and that therefore one would need even more little Ronnies to enable the top one to breathe – and therefore the Ronnie supply problem would be even greater. And before Brian could muster any sort of response to this pedantic assault, Sandra suggested that he should get on and ready himself for breakfast. There was, she went on to inform him, a 'disembarkation briefing' at 9.30, and they both needed to attend it. Only by doing so would they have any idea of when and how they would be leaving the ship tomorrow.

It was done; breakfast having been consumed, the briefing was received. They now knew that the disembarkation would be first thing tomorrow morning and that therefore packing would need to be performed today. Nevertheless, that would still leave much of the day to spend as they chose, and if they wanted to they could even attend a 'fruit carving and flambé demonstration' later that morning.

Well, as it transpired, this choice was not made. Sandra preferred to get the packing out of the way and Brian chose to stay out of her way – by getting to grips with some 'macaronic language'. It was down to the wife of the Latin pronunciation expert from the previous evening. At the end of that morning briefing, she had supplied him with some handwritten sheets of paper, and on these sheets were a few examples of something he had never been aware of before, the aforementioned 'curiosity' of macaronic language. Initially, he had difficulty in understanding what it was all about, but then it clicked. And what it was all about was playing with a mix of languages, and particularly using a word or phrase in one language that sounds similar to a different word or phrase in another language. And if that makes little sense, then more sense might be made by quoting a couple of the provided examples, the first of which was:

Caesar adsum jam forte
Brutus aderat
Caesar sic in omnibus
Brutus sic in at

That was apparently a Ronald Searle verse – and it really required a passing acquaintance with Latin. The following Luis d'Antin van Rooten example, in contrast, assumed a passing acquaintance with French – and a knowledge of the beginning of the 'Humpty Dumpty' poem. This was:

Un petit d'un petit
S'étonne aux Halles
Un petit d'un petit
Ah! degrés te falle

Well, this kept Brian amused for some time, not so much by the macaronic language itself, but by the fact that people would indulge in this sort of nonsense. It really cheered him that there were individuals on this planet who were prepared to invest their time and effort in such pointless diversions. And he was equally cheered that it had taken him a whole lifetime and an encounter on a ship in the Solomon Sea to discover the existence of this rather arcane discipline. Cruising did have a number of unexpected bonuses – and a few more that were not entirely unexpected, such as the sighting of a pod of pilot whales!

Yes. Sandra had seen them first, just before Garth, on the ship's PA system, had announced their presence. There were more than a dozen of them and they were only a couple of hundred yards from the ship's starboard side. And they were kept within this distance by the captain taking the *Caledonian Sky* into a leisurely 360-degree turn, at the end of which every passenger on his vessel had been provided with the best view possible of these remarkable creatures. And they are remarkable. These were short-finned pilot whales and they are actually dolphins and in size are the second biggest of all the dolphins after orcas. They are highly social and their strong social bonds have been cited as the reason that they so often end up stranded on beaches. It is thought that an entire pod might follow a sick member of the group who has become stranded or an 'important' member who has done the same. (Indeed, their name is derived from the belief that pods of these animals were 'piloted' by a leader.) Anyway, when not getting themselves into difficulty, they spend their time eating squid and fish, and only rarely are they seen with a leather flying hat and never with a handlebar moustache and a light blue cravat.

Inevitably, their appearance was discussed over lunch. Brian and Sandra had joined four others for this midday meal, and the initial topic of conversation concerned this recent dramatic sighting of cetaceans – and the revelation by one of the four, Keith, that these pilot whales are one of the few mammal species in which the females go through menopause. Brian found this new fact mildly interesting, but he then found the subsequent revelations distinctly upsetting. This was because they had been introduced by this same Keith, and they concerned another sea-living mammal – and its imminent demise...

He'd apparently read all about it before he'd come away on this trip, how the 'vaquita porpoise' is now down to a population of just thirty individuals. This poor critter, he told his fellow diners, has the misfortune to live in the Gulf of California, a World Heritage site that sits between the Mexican mainland and the Baja Peninsula – and which is fished by the Mexicans for something called the totoaba. This, Keith went on to explain, is a large fish which is prized for its swim bladder, not by anybody normal, of course, but by all those turds who make money out of preparing traditional (and despicable) Chinese medicine. It appears that these bladders are valued so much by these monsters that they will pay $8,500 a kilo for them on the black market, which is the sort of price that means Mexican fishermen will harvest them without any thought for the collateral damage they're causing. Even if this collateral damage is the extinction of a species. Because these fishermen know as well as anybody knows that vaquita porpoise numbers are down by 90% since 2011 (!) and that the reason for this collapse in their numbers is the use of gill nets to catch the totoaba. These are nets that are hung vertically to snare the fish by their gills, but which also snare and kill the porpoises. Which meant, Keith suggested, that it was quite difficult to decide who were the biggest blackguards; the callous Mexican fishermen, the turds who were using those swim bladders to make up their horrible Chinese potions – or all those hundreds of thousands of Chinese who buy these potions and don't give a fig about the natural world.

Brian said he thought it was the latter group, but that he'd still like to see the other two groups exterminated as well – rather than the remaining population of vaquita porpoises. The others agreed, and didn't even take exception to his wishing death on a host of people whom they had actually never met. Maybe, he thought, he wasn't quite as out of step in his thoughts as he'd imagined, and there were actually countless 'normal' people who found the behaviour of some of their fellow men so egregious that they regarded them as devoid of any real humanity and therefore not worthy of any degree of human compassion. And it was certainly difficult to argue that the world wouldn't be a better place without them. It might also be a world where Brian didn't find quite so many opportunities to fall into melancholia, into the sort of state of desolation that he was now experiencing as a direct result of learning about the plight of those poor porpoises and which, no doubt, would be wallowed in just as soon as he was back in his room.

He started immediately – while Sandra was fine-tuning the packing – and he knew immediately that his sadness was so great that it would need more than the plight of just one species to nourish it, but instead the plight of all non-human life on this Earth. And as he'd already considered the plight of the world's flora after his visit to Norfolk Island, he would now consider the plight of its fauna – all of it, other, of course, than mankind.

His starting point was the surface of the planet – including its seas – and the finite amount of life it could sustain. So... the more of 'us' there were, he believed, then no matter how careful we might be, the less of 'them' there would be. Quite simply, if we demand space to live, to grow our crops and to feed our domesticated animals, then many other animals are denied an equal amount of space. Countless 'non-useful' beasts are being nudged out. Or, in some parts of the world they have already been pushed out entirely, and unless they have the good fortune to be rats, mice, nits or lice they will probably never return.

Unfortunately, Brian reminded himself, it doesn't stop at our usurping their land. We've also played a blinder when it comes to something called 'the introduction of invasive species'. This has proved a real winner, it being something we can initiate and then just sit back and let take its course. We don't even have to participate in it to ensure it wreaks havoc.

What it is, of course, is the thoughtless or reckless introduction of a 'foreign' species into a new environment where it will establish itself and then affect the native species – by eating them, competing with them directly or by screwing up their habitat. And it works a treat. So much so that on a few occasions we haven't just sat back but we've actually played the invasive species ourselves. Yes, it might not be immediately apparent, Brian recalled, but when we arrived in places like Australia 40,000 years ago – or in North and South America just 12,000 years ago – we were barging in on environments full of animals that had never seen us before and were therefore completely at a loss as to how to deal with our particular 'predation techniques'. The result was the swift extinction of all the mega-fauna in almost half the world and a desire on the part of mankind to repeat its success elsewhere – with creatures such as mammoths and then a host of other animals in places like Madagascar and New Zealand. In fact, the only place where mega-fauna now exists in any worthwhile numbers is Africa, and to mop up this lot on a timely basis we cannot unfortunately rely on invading them as a pernicious species or even just usurping them. No. We will have to resort to the agency of climate change, ably assisted by out-of-control poaching...

At this stage of his musings, Brian was back to the blackguards again, those people who saw nothing wrong in bribing a Chinese official with an extravagant ivory carving, those others who wanted to stiffen their atrophied willies with extract of tiger or essence of seahorse, and yet others who regarded shopping for bear bile or pangolin parts as no different to shopping for mangoes. These literal savages weren't just accelerating the demise of scores of iconic animals but they were also spitting in the face of every enlightened member of the human race, all those men and women who see these animals for what they really are: the exquisite product of eons of evolution with as much right to a continued tenancy on this planet as any upright ape. And nowhere is there a reserve stock or a back-up supply. Once these wonders have gone, they will have gone – permanently – and no amount of traditional Chinese junk will ever bring them back.

Brian now felt *really* depressed. Whether we were seizing their land, screwing up their existence with introduced species, exterminating them through some form of pollution or brutally killing them for the supposed benefit of our health or our willies, we had now graduated to an 'event', and for all non-human life on the planet, the worst sort of event imaginable, commonly known as an extinction event. We won't need giant asteroids any more or some sort of powerful supernova, but instead we can just continue to steamroller forward with an increase in our numbers, continue to be careless and stupid in how we treat our environment – and continue to be barbaric in our behaviour to rhinos, elephants, sharks, tigers, pangolins, snakes and a thousand or so other endangered species. And the real killer – for Brian – was that whatever he did he knew that he himself was part of this extinction event, part of the process of wiping out much of the life on this planet – and wiping out all of its magic. And no amount of boycotting Hong Kong restaurants which sold shark fin soup was about to change that. It depressed him to hell.

Well, there was only one thing to do. He would write some more limericks. He would immerse himself in more of his poetic endeavours until it was time for dinner. That way, he might just free himself from his melancholia and not be entirely miserable throughout the meal.

It worked. When he and Sandra gathered in the Caledonian Lounge for their last pre-dinner drink – with Thor, Lise, Paul and Lydia – he was feeling positively sunny. And when Paul then suggested that all six of them should make an early departure to the Bridge Deck restaurant to ensure that they could secure a shared table for this, their last meal together, he became even sunnier. So when they were all seated and the meal was about to start, it was as though he'd never been melancholic in his life. All he felt was real happiness, and all he wanted to do was enjoy this Melanesian last supper as much as he could.

In fact, the meal went very well. The food was excellent and everybody around the table was in top form, all of them eager to make their own contribution to this last evening together. Lise was first in with the observation that if one 'ignores' something then one has made a positive choice to do so, in the sense that one is free to ignore something or not to ignore it. It follows then, she suggested, that the product of ignoring – which is ignorance – is also a matter of choice. One can either be ignorant or one can be informed and knowledgeable

– and enlightened. Then, having made this point, she went on to bemoan the fact that, for so many people, the default setting now seemed to be 'ignore as much as possible', with the result that most of mankind is ignorant beyond belief.

She illustrated this point with a reference to what she had observed back home: people who were unable to distinguish between a paedophile and a paediatrician, people who were more than a little hazy about Churchill's role in World War II – and simply puzzled as to how an inanimate nodding dog could have had such a huge impact on the course of that war – and other people who, when asked what Absolute Zero was, could only think that it was a new programme on Channel 4 designed to establish which of the failed *X Factor* contestants was the most dismal of all. Worse still was the fact that these people rejoiced in their ignorance, and were almost proud that they knew little more than which bunch of idiots were currently flashing their distempered teeth in *The Only Way Is Essex*. Because, Lise explained, we are now into the arena of 'if it's not trending, I haven't a clue' or 'if it involves reading, listening carefully, concentrating for more than two seconds or putting my brain into gear, then count me out'.

She now had the attention of all her table companions. After all, they had not heard her talk like this before. However, she had some even sterner stuff to say yet. Because she then went on to propose that it was one thing to be under the impression that horticulture is something only posh people have, but quite another to be unable to distinguish between basic decency and a blatant travesty of natural justice. Here, Lise had in mind all those millions of men around the world who would happily read their holy scripts but who were never quite so keen to engage their brains, and whose resulting ignorance was the cause of untold suffering for millions of women. Yes, she concluded, ignorance was not just a matter of choice, but it was also a pandemic, an affliction of mankind as likely to be found in the backstreets of Cairo as in the nail bars of Romford. And was there any way to curb it?

Well, no, there wasn't. That was the general feeling around the table. One just had to learn to accept that ignorance was ubiquitous and almost a badge of honour – even though it was a genuine scourge – and get on with one's life, and maybe consider another scourge of this world – such as that persistent overpopulation problem. This was Paul's suggestion, and he made this suggestion because he claimed that he had come up with a novel idea as to how the problem could be solved. This, he announced, was the use of genetic modification to greatly increase the gestation period of the human mammal. And he soon made clear that he wasn't thinking of doubling the 270 days of a human to say the 535 of a sperm whale, but to something of the order of 3,000 days, so that when little Freddie popped out he would look something like an eight-year-old.

He did accept that GM technology had some way to go, and that there would be other problems to overcome, problems such as the necessary fortification of the female frame, the acceptance of Caesarean births as the norm and the inevitable challenges of… multiple

225

births. However, he maintained, the benefits would be enormous. First and foremost, the birth rate would be slashed, probably within a generation. After all, there was no way, he argued, that a woman who had carried a bloody great baby for eight years would want more than two of the things and many would stick at just one. In this way the world's human overload would at last be relieved. And furthermore, there would be huge savings on childcare costs, on education costs, on birthday celebration costs – and there wouldn't be all those overgrown pushchairs blocking the pavements.

Well, this radical idea earned itself an enthusiastic response, but only from Brian and Thor. The women at the table were less seduced by Paul's novel solution to the overpopulation problem, possibly because they focused more on its likely teething problems than they did on its enormous benefits. Or maybe they were able to empathise with an improbably pregnant woman more than the men could. And for one of them, the topic of childbirth – and the use of genetic modification – triggered a completely different train of thought, and this concerned the shifting of responsibilities between the genders…

This was Lydia, and her argument was that if GM could achieve all manner of ungodly outcomes already, wouldn't there be the likelihood, in the not too distant future, of men being able to become effective (albeit possibly reluctant) living incubators. Childbearing could then be shared, and overnight women would achieve real equality with their male counterparts – and males would begin to understand how lucky they had been in the past, when their investment in the procreation process had been confined to just a few minutes of intense pleasure. There would clearly be a few 'mechanical' problems involved, conceded Lydia, and she also admitted that the loading and unloading processes would have to be worked out. But notwithstanding these minor details, she maintained that her idea was a brilliant one, not least because when men had experienced the childbearing role themselves, they would be far less willing to countenance large families and this would inevitably have the effect of reducing the world's population – but without causing women to develop bow legs and a back problem as they would if Paul's idea got off the ground.

This time it was the men at the table who could assemble little enthusiasm – or even much of a response. Which is why Sandra rode to the rescue with an entirely new topic. This concerned driverless cars and, when they had begun to appear in numbers, whether they would be able to engage in courteous behaviour…

Like everybody else around the table, she was at a loss to understand why anybody would want a driverless car in the first place and why presumably young people seemed so eager to jettison what could be one of the real pleasures of life: the piloting of a responsive motor car and thereby the facility to experience what was undisputedly a unique relationship between man and machine. However, she accepted that if the technology existed it would be introduced whatever she thought – or whatever young people thought – and our roads would ultimately become populated by 'machine-driven' vehicles.

And so to her point, which she illustrated by describing how she went about her own driving – in a conventional car. And what she said was that when, on the road, she saw another car in a side road to her left, its driver waiting for a good-mannered driver to let him pull out, she would slow down, flash him with her lights and let him emerge. He would wave a thanks, she would wave back and both would feel just a little bit happier to be alive. Furthermore, she emphasised, the traffic generally would run far more smoothly and the likelihood of gridlock would be reduced. The 'good-turn-lubricant' was no less than essential. So, she wondered, would a driverless car be able to engage in this behaviour, and even if it could, would a driverless car on the receiving end of the courteous gesture recognise it as this, and if not would it ignore it and just sit in the side road indefinitely?

Well, this wasn't one of the great philosophical questions of the day, but it was an important question, at least for all those poor sods whose life was to be spent in an automated traffic system and who would never be able to relish the pure joy of controlling a vehicle and every other aspect of the true driving experience.

It was also a question that nobody around the table could answer, albeit they all shared Sandra's doubts as to whether driverless vehicle technology would ever become clever enough to be courteous. Thor suggested that this was about as likely as Mr Trump ever becoming clever enough to be courteous, which of course was never going to happen. What might happen instead, he postulated, was it coming to light that Donald J

Trump was none other than a disguised Kim Jong-un, the supreme leader of North Korea and the perennial winner of the annual world's worst haircut award.

This was a radical proposition that merited some explanation, and Thor provided this by first pointing out that Donald has the same ample conformation as Kim, the same 'generous' facial dimensions, the same affection for bluster and nonsense, the same complete lack of rational thought processes – and, just like Clark Kent and Superman, Don and Kim have never been seen together!

Brian and Paul thought that this reasoning was pretty convincing, but it was the women again who wanted to pour cold water on this startling insight, led, on this occasion, by Sandra. She first doused Thor's possibly perceptive powers by pointing out that if Don and Kim were actually one and the same person seeking to appear as two, then there was no way that Kim would have chosen a haircut for his alter-ego role that was as ridiculous as his own. It would be too much of a giveaway. And, she went on, there was also the question of logistics, to say nothing of those of language, accent, respective replicants and all sorts of other things.

Yes, Sandra, Lise and Lydia all rejected Thor's idea outright – and quickly formulated a new idea – which was that President Trump was actually Kim Don-dum, Kim Jong-un's secret brother, a scion of old Kim Jong-il, hidden from the world until he could be surgically degraded, provided with a small vocabulary of locker-room American, programmed to be as puerile and incompetent as could possibly be imagined and then installed in the White House. And here he would sit for four years and do far more damage to the US than his brother and his assorted weapons could do to that country in 400 years.

Nobody challenged this proposition. In fact it met with universal agreement, at which point Brian thought it was about time that he added his own two-pennyworth to this evening's erudite exchange. He did this by asking his table companions whether they had given any thought to props in the last few years and did any of them know whether one could still buy them?

This question was met with total puzzlement until Brian went on to explain that the 'props' he had in mind here were those wooden clothes-line props (with a notch at their end) which had been used by all good housewives to support their fully loaded clothes lines and to expose the various clothes suspended therefrom to the full drying power of a Monday morning breeze. Puzzlement then turned to bemusement as Brian went on to give voice to his thoughts about the possible elevation of clothes props to items of historical importance – along with washboards and mangles – and the possible elevation in their worth. What value, he wondered, might Hilary Kay ascribe to a showroom-condition clothes prop from the fifties if presented with one on the *Antiques Roadshow*? Or how about one that came with a royal pedigree or one that was owned by Dylan Thomas and was known to have been used when he was writing *Under Milk Wood*?

Well, his reflections on washing-day aids were brought to an abrupt end by Lise informing him that props did still exist – albeit they were now made of metal not of wood – and they could, of course, be purchased from Amazon. But it didn't really matter. What mattered was that six people had come together on a two-week cruise and had graduated to the stage where they could sit and exchange all sorts of nonsense and thereby enjoy each other's company to the absolute utmost. In Brian's mind, it was possibly the very best aspect of the cruise – as it was with Sandra. She told him so when they were back in their cabin – after the meal and just before he started on his next round of limericks. These were as follows:

An Aussie young lady would wonder
Why it was that her suitors all shunned her
'Til a friend pointed out
That without any doubt
They'd all hoped that they'd see her down under

And

There was a young man called Bob Hunt
Who planned to have sex in a punt
But he thought just in time
Of an indecent rhyme
So he settled for just a loud grunt

And

There was a young woman from Norway
Who didn't think much about foreplay

Then Ken came around
And that's when she found
How much it could open her doorway

And

There was a young creep called Delors
Who spied through the keyholes of doors
And in this way he found
That all housewives were bound
To keep certain stuff in their drawers

Sandra passed judgement. This was 'vulgar, vulgar, vulgar and completely vulgar in that order'.

Praise indeed, thought Brian. And the trip wasn't over yet. There was still time to do even better. In fact, he'd give it some thought straightaway. And maybe he'd begin by sorting out what rhymed with 'prop'...

16.

hen Brian awoke, his first thought was that North Korea has the same initials as 'naughty knickers', and his second thought was that the DPRK, as North Korea is officially known, could also stand for 'decidedly provocative *raunchy* knickers'. Then he had a third thought. This was that he should get out of bed, push from his mind what were clearly the warped after-effects of Thor's speculation of the previous evening and instead ready himself for the disembarkation from the *Caledonian Sky*. After all, there was the packing to finalise, some ablutions to conduct, a breakfast to eat and then an end of a voyage to witness. And he certainly didn't want to miss that...

The *Caledonian Sky* was now approaching Rabaul, its chosen port of disembarkation and, as Brian already knew, Rabaul, whilst undisputedly a port in Papua New Guinea, was not a port in mainland Papua New Guinea. No, instead it was situated at the extreme eastern end of 'New Britain', and New Britain is the banana-shaped island that sits to the east of mainland PNG and to the west of a thin, banana-shaped island (also part of PNG) called... 'New Ireland'. In fact, it had recently occurred to Brian that if one took account of these two offshore elements of PNG, together with New Caledonia and what used to be the New Hebrides (now Vanuatu), one would only need to find a New Isle of Wight, a New Isle of Man and a New other-bits-of-offshore-Scotland, and one would have all one needed to create a complete-in-all-respects New British Isles. Not one that was off the coast of northern Europe but one that was situated at the heart of Melanesia.

But anyway, apart from Brian's idle musings, what this meant was that whilst the cruising element of this trip was about to conclude, there was still at least half a day more to be spent in what was still undeniably… Melanesia. And this was because it wasn't until late afternoon that he and Sandra would be flying out of New Britain. Like most of the ship's other passengers, they were scheduled to depart for Queensland later in the day (while a smaller number were about to spend a few days in mainland Papua New Guinea and just a handful were staying on board the *Caledonian Sky* for its next – and imminent – voyage up through the Indonesian and Philippine archipelagos). However, that was not his immediate concern. For now he was more interested in what would be the mirror image of that departure from Auckland: the *Caledonian Sky*'s approach to Rabaul, and what would be the end of a sea trip of over 3,000 nautical miles. And what's more, the weather was perfect. There was a startlingly blue sky above and a mirror-smooth sea below that, together with Rabaul's magical setting, would make it difficult for both Brian and Sandra ever to forget this mirror image arrival.

'Magical', Brian pondered, was not a word to use

lightly, but that was exactly the word that had popped into his mind as the *Caledonian Sky* came within just miles of this final anchorage. And this was because Rabaul sits at the back of a nearly enclosed, fabulously beautiful, natural harbour, which itself is overlooked by two fearsome but stunning-looking volcanoes. The result is more Hollywood-imagined South Pacific paradise than anything real. But it is real – as real as those two soddin' great volcanoes, those two overbearing near neighbours that have made Rabaul anything but a paradise to live in. Yes, the approach to Rabaul was unforgettably splendid, but it was the approach to a settlement that shouldn't really be there – and one day might not be, thanks solely to the likely future behaviour of 'Tavurvur' and 'Vulcan', the terrible twins from 'volcano world' that even now threaten to erase it entirely.

They had a pretty good go in 1937 when they exploded and killed over 500 people and caused some very extensive damage. Then they really went for it in 1994, by which time Rabaul's magnificent harbour and its ideal position as a site for a trading hub had seen its population grow to over 17,000. This time their joint eruption was so large that it overwhelmed Rabaul's airport and at the same time it dumped so much ash on the town itself that many of its buildings collapsed under the weight. It didn't, however, manage to kill that many people, largely because the town's occupants had learnt how dangerous the terrible twins could be and they had been practising evacuation drills for years. They also intended to stay where they were after the event, and although their town lost its status as a provincial capital and their airport had to be rebuilt quite a few miles away, they opted for a reconstruction programme – together with the establishment of a government-run seismic observatory. Here the mood of what are two of the most active and most dangerous volcanoes in all of Papua New Guinea is now monitored continuously – while the people of Rabaul go about their business and sometimes, no doubt, stop to consider what a wonderful, if precarious, place they have chosen to live in.

Inevitably, as the *Caledonian Sky* got ever nearer to Rabaul, it didn't look quite as wonderful. The natural harbour was still spectacular and the twin volcanoes were still impressive, but Rabaul itself looked a little dishevelled and its dockside looked more than dishevelled. It looked positively abandoned. Nevertheless, there upon it were signs of its re-adoption – in the form of a clutch of diminutive minibuses and a similar clutch of pickups. Brian just hoped that the minibuses would be used to ferry him and his fellow passengers around Rabaul and that the pickups would be employed to take their combined luggage to the distant airport – and not the other way round. He certainly had no desire to repeat his experience of transport on Tanna. Well, in the event, all was exactly as he'd hoped for. After a copious round of goodbyes at the foot of the ship's gangway – to all the principals in the *Caledonian Sky* production and to all those passengers who were not going on to Queensland – Brian and his fellow travellers were squeezed into the minibuses, while their assorted cases were provided with rather more capacious accommodation on the back of the pickups.

There was no getting away from it. The minibuses were genuinely... mini. In fact, Brian and Sandra's was so mini, that Brian was provided with the only seat that could almost accommodate his overlong legs – which was the passenger seat in the minibus cab – and Sandra was obliged to sit next to him on the engine cover that separated him from the driver. This enabled Brian to give some immediate and serious thought to the desirability or otherwise of restorative knee surgery and Sandra to do the same in respect of the accepted cultural norms relating to the close but innocent contact with an unaccompanied local male. He really was close to Sandra – but not quite as close as the gear stick was to her thigh. And he had wonderfully red teeth. Like many Papuans, he was a chewer of betel nuts, and this nicotine analogue provides not only a nicotine-type hit to those who chew it but also gloriously red-stained mouths – and scarlet gnashers. And what were the accepted cultural norms relating to scarlet grins? The driver of the minibus seemed to speak no English, but he did grin a lot – at Sandra – particularly when he was changing gear, and Sandra was at a loss as to how to respond. Should she grin back? Should she hide her offensively white teeth? Should she offer to change gear occasionally? Or should she just stare through the front windscreen and, like her husband, focus on downtown Rabaul? In the event she opted for the latter. Not that there was much to focus on.

It was all a bit laid-back scruffy with a sprinkling of civic good intent in the form of roadside shrub planting and the odd painted kerb. That said, in Brian's mind, it was infinitely more ordered and cared for than many other settlements he'd seen in the world, and it was notable for its complete lack of either squalor or acute dilapidation. At this point he chided himself for setting such a low bar in his assessment of this urban environment, but the fact remained that Papua New Guinea was not a rich country and Rabaul was about as distant from its capital and its major source of wealth as it was possible to be – and much of the world is simply nothing like one finds in the Cotswolds. It is full of some pretty nasty towns and villages. Furthermore, it was steaming hot in Rabaul, and undertaking any sort of urban enhancements or just keeping things tidy must have taken more energy and effort than Brian could ever have mustered himself.

So, he ended up deciding that he was actually giving the locals a well-earned if somewhat backhanded compliment – although they still had a little way to go on the state of their roads, especially those leading out of town.

Yes, the squadron of minibuses was now heading out of built-up Rabaul into the countryside, and the road being used for this departure was not of the highest standard. Brian had to brace himself in his seat and Sandra had to hold on to anything inanimate she could find. Then the road became a track and the bracing and the holding moved up a notch. Brian just hoped that wherever they were going wasn't too far away, and then he saw that they were heading for the twin volcanoes! Surely they weren't going there. Surely they weren't going to provoke those terrible towering twins…

Well, no, they weren't. They were just going to visit some hot springs. In fact, the minibuses had soon come to a halt where the track had suddenly widened out into an ash field, in the middle of which was the object of the excursion: a small stream of near-boiling water flowing through a rusty-coloured channel. Everybody was soon off the buses and, if they were anything like Brian, soon appreciating how furiously hot it was here – even though it was still early morning. Indeed it was so hot and so exposed at this site that most of the party spent the first few minutes of their visit either organising some protection from the sun or equipping themselves with water bottles. Quite a few of them then spent the remaining few minutes worrying about the fact that the scores of locals who were already here and hoping to sell some of their local handicrafts had neither of these essentials. They were just sitting on the ash, their wares spread out before them, and none of them seemed to have any water or any means of providing themselves with shade. And to make matters worse, they were finding no buyers within the party of visitors. It was, in Brian's opinion, all rather grim. OK, the stream of boiling water was mildly interesting and its situation in an ash field that was bordered by the sea and overlooked by Tavurvur was certainly quite dramatic, but the overriding recollection of this place for Brian would be of a bunch of very poor people (most of whom were women) enduring the completely unendurable just to make a few pennies or no pennies at all. Indeed for the first time on this trip, Brian felt like a really rich bastard breezing his way through a world of paupers and he didn't much like it. In fact, no more than he liked the fact that he so much relished the air conditioning as he squeezed back onto the bus, while all those poor women outside were left to fry under a tropical sun. And he could do nothing about it – other than hope that it didn't kick off another bout of melancholia.

Well, it didn't, possibly because within just a few minutes of the minibuses pulling away from the ash field, they were turning off the road back into town to pay a visit to one of the few buildings that had survived the 1994 eruption: the almost imposing clubhouse of the 'New Guinea Club'. It had clearly seen better days – when, years ago, it had served as a focal point for this country's colonial masters. Now, it had no paying members at all, no club committee, nobody to ensure the adherence to club rules and no chance of getting a nice cool lager or a glass of pink gin. And this was because its club days were now long gone and its present role was to act as a local museum and to tell the story not only of its colonial past but also of the significance of Rabaul during the Second World War.

Brian learnt a lot here, not just from the dusty reminders of the past that now filled the building but also from those in his party who had done their Rabaul homework. And to start with he learnt that this modest-looking port was captured by the Japanese in 1942 and then used as the main base for their military and naval activity in the South Pacific in the following three years. This involved their building all sorts of facilities here, including an airfield, and also building up the number of troops here, until by 1943 there were 110,000 of the little blighters in and around the port – including the guy who had masterminded the Japanese attack on Pearl Harbor, one Admiral Isoroku Yamamoto.

Of course, it all ended in tears. Not only did the Japanese lose the war but their heavily defended facilities in Rabaul were simply bypassed by the Allied forces in their advance towards Japan itself, and they were then contained by the Allies through their surrounding the place with a ring of airfields and naval bases. Oh, and of course even that airfield they built that served as Rabaul airport after the war ended up under ash, and so much ash that it is now invisible. That's why Brian had not known that when he was being driven down that track to the hot springs earlier this morning, he had at the same time been rolling down the carpet of ash that now covered the airfield's main runway. It was buried down there below the wheels of the minibus, along with all those Imperial Japanese ambitions of the past and probably the odd bottle of sake and some fossilised noodles.

Anyway, it was now time to move on from the museum and drive back through Rabaul, this time to pay a visit to its seismic observatory. This involved a climb up a winding road, past a series of tunnels built by the Japanese during the war, until the observatory appeared, as did a panoramic view of Rabaul's natural harbour. It was spellbinding – the panoramic view that is – and it also afforded a view of the *Caledonian Sky,* still at anchor at the quayside and no doubt still being re-provisioned for its onward voyage further north. It was the sight of this ship at a distance that finally prompted

Brian to recognise how sad he was to have left this fabulous vessel. It had been a joy to be aboard it, but there had been just too much going on and too many goodbyes as he'd left it this morning to register what he was in the process of giving up: a privileged existence on a beautiful pocket cruise ship that he would probably never experience again. It didn't make him actually melancholic, but it did make him feel a little morose and it definitely took the edge off his visit to the observatory itself. This was a modest building, full of seismic-type equipment and manned by a couple of local and very pleasant seismologists who, Brian thought, must have welcomed any sort of visit to their workplace to relieve the monotony. And how, he thought, would they react if one day 'things livened up', if their machines told them that they could soon expect some imminent volcanic activity and the possible obliteration of Rabaul? With terror? With excitement? With unrestrained relief that after all these fucking years of watching these damned machines something was finally going to happen? Well, probably with terror, possibly laced with just the smallest soupçon of excitement – and the smallest soupçon of 'am I now out of a job?' It certainly wouldn't, he decided, be with either indifference or glee.

He also decided that this tour of Rabaul and its environs was turning into another tour of Auckland, in the sense that a certain time had to be filled before the happy campers could be sent on their way – this time in an aeroplane rather than a ship. And this view of their minibus odyssey was reinforced when said campers were driven back into town and deposited at Rabaul's open-

242

air market, there to consume another tranche of waiting time by wandering between its stalls. Well, Brian was being unduly churlish – again – because what became apparent almost immediately was that Rabaul market had about as much in common with that dreadful and depressing market back in Honiara as D J Trump Esq had in common with any well-balanced and thoughtful human being. It was a genuinely vibrant and attractive place. Not only did the produce on offer look appealing, but those selling it looked really happy and were more than pleased to smile and to make eye contact with a saturated visitor and his wife. Yes, that was the market's only drawback. Being outside, it was of course not air-conditioned, and consequently its ambient temperature and humidity were more than enough to ensure that Brian was in full drip mode and so much so that ultimately he could barely see where he was going due to the pooling of perspiration in his eyes. He was now in full flow.

Brian was therefore pretty relieved to be back in his air-conditioned minibus can, and even further relieved to learn that the can would now be setting off for the airport. Not the buried one under the shadow of those two volcanoes but the replacement airport which had been built over forty kilometres away near a town called Tokua. That was fine, although he did soon realise that if the airport was over forty kilometres away, that meant a trip of this distance along a road that might not be quite up to motorway standards. And it wasn't. It was more like the curate's egg – or should that be a particularly bad curate's egg? Which is to say that it was good in (a very few) parts and otherwise pretty well abysmal, with whole sections of it washed away and essentially non-existent. It would have been a struggle in a top-end 4x4. In a packed, underpowered 'miniature-mobile', it was a real trial.

Nevertheless, the driver of Brian and Sandra's miniature-mobile continued to flash those bright red teeth and ultimately he coaxed his little vehicle over all the obstacles in its path and, with the rest of his squadron, he delivered his passengers to another club. And this club was still a club and not a museum. As far as Brian could tell it was on the outskirts of Tokua and it was some sort of (Chinese-run) sports club. Who used it he could not tell, but it did have a restaurant – and it did have a bar. It was therefore very welcome, as were the beers that Brian secured after he'd visited the club's bureau de change to buy some PNG currency! And the food wasn't too bad either.

This lunchtime stop consumed another hour of waiting time, after which it was made clear that the next stop would be the last stop – at Rabaul airport. It took no more than ten minutes to get there – and no more than sixty minutes to check in…

The party's luggage, which had been brought here in those pickups, was awaiting collection. Then it had to be shepherded into the airport's check-in area where it was able to keep its owners company as they each lost an average of three pounds in body weight – all of it in the form of liquid. The trouble was that the airport's computer had either died or was flat on its back after an overdose of betel nut, and the check-in process had to be conducted with the use of a pencil and a bit of paper. This wouldn't have been so bad if the check-in area wasn't doubling up as a heavy-duty Turkish bath, one that made that recent visit to a market seem like a stroll in a chilly park. It was unbelievably hot and humid and by the time most people had finally got through the check-in ordeal they were not only lighter but their clothes were considerably heavier, as each fibre of material from which they were made had captured and stored all the sweat it could possibly manage. And what's more, the only flight from this airport this afternoon was the single charter flight that would take this collection of soaking travellers off to Queensland. Had there been more than one flight, Brian dreaded to think what would have been the result – and how many of the group would have ended up entirely desiccated and looking like a collection of human crisps.

Well, Brian could, on occasions, exaggerate just a little, but he couldn't have exaggerated the difference in temperature between that in the airport and that in the plane. And this was because the temperature in the plane's cabin was more Melton Mowbray than Melanesia – as in Melton Mowbray on a brisk February morning. Yes, as soon as Brian had left Melanesia behind him he had found himself in a flying fridge. Furthermore, he had neglected to pack his thermals and instead was sitting in a pair of wet shorts and a wet T-shirt. The result: two hours of purgatory as the plane winged its way to Cairns, and a desperate need to distract himself – with what else but some more limerick writing.

This literary labour did help a little, but not a lot.

Neither did the chilly temperature in Cairns airport. And then, when Brian and Sandra boarded a full-sized coach to ferry them to their Cairns hotel, matters got significantly worse. It reminded Brian of a time decades ago when he had been taken into the chilling room of an ice cream factory – where they harden off the ice cream through the use of super-cooled air blown through a super-strength blower. In this coach, the blower was in its ceiling just above Brian's head and it really did have the capacity to harden off ice cream or at least Brian's attitudes to the overuse of air conditioning in warmer climes.

By the time Brian and Sandra had made it to their (overly air-conditioned) room in the hotel, Brian was thoroughly chilled, not to say friggin' frozen, which is probably why he began to shiver uncontrollably…

Fantastic! Spend two weeks in the Tropics and end up with hypothermia. He couldn't have made it up. And he didn't need to, because it was real. Sandra therefore suggested that he get into bed and wrap himself up in the duvet, which is exactly what he did without any hesitation whatsoever. He really didn't want to die before he'd reached a hundred or before he'd recited his latest limericks – whichever came first.

Anyway, an hour later, he'd recovered enough to stop the uncontrollable shaking and enough to present his solicitous wife with the product of his earlier airborne limerick endeavours. These were:

There was a young lady from Hants
Who just yearned for a bit of romance

And if not true *amour*
Then at least rather more
Than 'Eh luv, what's this in yer pants?'

And then the even more delicate:

There was a young lady called Doris
Whose passion lay with her clitoris
She caressed it most days
– And in all sorts of ways –
And she gave it a name – which was Boris

Sandra almost smiled, but then she advised her husband to avoid any sort of poetic exertions on any super-cooled planes. The combination of the cabin air pressure and the cabin temperature clearly removed any remnants of decency he retained while still on the ground – and the result was rather more than unfortunate.

Brian thought his wife might be ribbing him. She had, after all, nearly smiled. And anyway, those two limericks weren't that bad. Nor was the fact that as well as forsaking Melanesia he also seemed to have forsaken melancholia! It was true. Despite some challenging aspects of the day just gone, he hadn't experienced even a hint of true melancholia and now felt just happy and content if just a wee bit sad that he might never be visiting Melanesia again.

He would, however, be visiting his limerick writing again. If he included the three limericks that had featured in the limerick competition he had now produced forty-nine of these little gems on this trip. And wouldn't it be sad, he thought, if he couldn't make it a round fifty? So that was his target: one more limerick before he and Sandra left Cairns in three days' time – and the sort of limerick that would finally make Sandra smile – or despair – or both.

Oh, and there was some of Cairns and the Queensland coast to explore as well, along with the possibility of buying some long johns and maybe a winter-grade thermal vest…

17.

*W*ell, thanks to Sandra's persistence with the air-con controls, Brian awoke to his first Cairns morning feeling just comfortable and no longer in need of thermal underwear. No, all he felt in need of was a decent breakfast. Neither he nor Sandra had eaten properly since lunchtime yesterday, and they were both now really hungry. This wasn't a problem. Although that bout of hypothermia had caused Brian to sleep until nine, the hotel's restaurant was open until ten-thirty. It said so in the in-room hotel directory. So when they arrived at this restaurant at just ten to ten, they knew that there would still be plenty of time to eat all they wanted. Or there would have been had the restaurant's closing time not been changed to nine-thirty…

Now, this hotel wasn't some cheapo place up a back street. It was the Cairns Hilton and it promised international standards, and as far as Brian was concerned that meant it couldn't clip an hour off its advertised breakfast slot without any notice. The restaurant manager disagreed – and was disagreeable. She would not budge and she would certainly not win any employee of the month award in the 'customer satisfaction' category. She just didn't care. Nor, for that matter, did the room service guy at the other end of the phone when Brian rang him from his room to order a room service breakfast – which was available until eleven. Or rather, it had been last week until they'd shaved an hour off that as well. And, as it was now just after ten, room service breakfasts were 'off'.

To his credit, Brian didn't become melancholic, but just rather annoyed and more determined than ever to squeeze some sort of breakfast out of this dreadful hotel. And he did – with the help of one of the reps from the tour operators. She shared his displeasure at the hotel's performance but she had a little more clout than Brian and Sandra on their own. The result: an enormous plate of sad pastries and other unappealing comestibles delivered to their room, which did fill a gap but which, at the same time, did make Brian wish that Australia had been colonised by France rather than Britain. Had those Frenchies been here first, he thought, no way would a pile of such unappetising victuals have been presented for consumption. Everything on the oversized breakfast tray looked completely uninviting and undeniably 'unsophisticated' in a way that would probably have constituted a crime back in France. And the croissant lookalikes certainly would have.

It hadn't been the best start to the day, but with the benefit of hindsight Brian would come to see that it was no more than a signpost to what would prove to be his and Sandra's experience of Cairns in general. This view, it has to be said, did border on the churlish and was possibly even well over the border and slap bang in the middle of churlistan, but it was unavoidable. Or at least it was for Brian, and it was based on what he saw as the disparity between what one observed in Cairns and what one experienced in Cairns.

The Hilton Hotel was beautiful and it was situated in a beautiful, waterside position. However, as already reported, its hospitality credentials were sadly lacking and, as would become apparent when Brian and Sandra did make it down in time for a breakfast, its food offerings were no better than those that had arrived on a room service tray. At best they could be described as ordinary, and at worst, as mean – and a million miles from what had been provided on the *Caledonian Sky*. Well, like the hotel, Cairns itself was beautiful. Indeed, it is probably one of the most beautiful and certainly one of the cleanest cities in the world. It has lots of greenery, lots of fine buildings, a splendid waterfront and lots of attractive waterfront restaurants, but not much… well, finesse. And this lack of finesse was at its most obvious in those waterfront restaurants where, despite being given a good Aussie welcome, one was then served with food that was as parsimonious in its appeal as it was generous in its proportions. Subtlety and even seasoning had not yet found their way into the kitchens of Cairns.

Now, Brian had not been kind in his assessment of Hong Kong and he was now being less than kind in his evaluation of what was an infinitely nicer place – apparently just on the basis of its cuisine. But this is not quite accurate, because there was another feature of his stay in Queensland that may well have pushed him to

251

form such a jaundiced and possibly such an unfair view of his time in this city – and this involved crabs…

The first full day in Cairns was spent in Cairns – absorbing its ambience and preparing to bitch about its lack of refinement. The second full day was spent outside Cairns and involved an organised 'full-day' expedition to the Daintree Rainforest to the north of Cairns. This was led by a really nice local Aussie and it was shared with about a dozen other souls, most of whom were former passengers from the *Caledonian Sky*. It was great – up until lunchtime. The rainforest was beautiful and there was even a close-up encounter with a fabulous amethystine python. But then lunchtime arrived – with another disappointing offering of food – to be followed thereafter by a move from the rainforest to the nearby coast where, as was announced by the Aussie leader, the afternoon was to be spent spearing crabs!

At first Brian thought that this was a very poor attempt at Australian humour. But it wasn't. The leader was being deadly serious. A local Aborigine was apparently awaiting their arrival and when they did arrive he would equip them all with spears and then take them into the coastal mangroves where said crabs would be perforated to death.

Brian didn't think that this was a very good idea and that it had about as much to do with a visit to a rainforest as an orgasm does with filling in a tax return. Sandra agreed and then they both agreed that when they got to the coast they would play the party poopers and have nothing to do with the crab-stabbing excursion and instead embark on a trudge to the highest moral ground they could find and from there cast their disdainful looks down on all those who had not been blessed with their superior wisdom and their superior self-righteousness. And that is exactly what they did. As William (the Aborigine) appeared, they excused themselves and retired to his home, there to await the return of the inexcusable hunting party – and to learn a little more about Aboriginal life in this part of Australia.

Well, the first thing they learnt was that the local Aborigines – William included – had a fondness for quite substantial houses and expensive 4x4s. His own home was not insubstantial in the least and was littered with all sorts of material goodies including the aforementioned 4x4s. It also had a balcony, which is where Brian and Sandra deposited themselves and began to inspect William's collection of turtle shells and, as reflected in a marked-up calendar, his collection of relatives. He had lots of both. Lots and lots of both. And Brian began to suspect that life was good for William – and for all those in his much wider family.

This suspicion was reinforced when one of his brothers appeared with a couple of American tourists and began to explain how he and his relatives were allowed to 'harvest' some of the local protected wildlife (because it was in their culture) and how they were very careful in making use of this incredible privilege by taking sea turtles and dugongs only when there was a big family gathering in the offing, something like a wedding or a christening party. Brian was not impressed. This family had so many members, weddings and christenings must have been a weekly event. Furthermore, William and his hunting party finally arrived back and the first thing William did – before he started cooking his 'stab victims' – was to go into the kitchen and reappear with a bowl of cold turtle pie, which he then offered to his rather bemused guests. And apparently it had not been left over from any family celebration. It was 'just there'.

Brian began to feel *really* bad. Not only was he being (probably) overly judgemental but he was also being (probably) marginally racist. However the fact remained that the Aussie leader of the group was being inexplicably deferential to their Aboriginal hosts and that these hosts seemed to be taking the piss. They seemed to be making the most of being Australians – very well – and at the same time the most of being a supposedly oppressed minority that had been granted all sorts of rights that would never be granted to any of their paler fellow cobbers. And anyway, the idea of turning wonders of the sea into pies – when there was no need to do so – was so fucking awful that Brian didn't really care that he was being marginally racist. All he cared about was seeing this 'rainforest visit' at an end and putting as many miles as possible between himself and the perpetrators of needless harm and suffering. Oh, and with Sandra, he had his self-righteous credentials to polish up as well.

Back in Cairns, Brian's mood did finally improve. After all, it wasn't as though everything about this place was bad. Not by any means. Indeed if the world outside Melanesia – as represented here by Cairns – was all like Cairns, it would be a veritable paradise (cuisine excepted). And Cairns did have some really positive points on top of its elegance and its cleanliness. It had, for example, every evening, a fantastic wildlife display in the shape of thousands of fruit bats flying into town to feed. And it also furnished Brian and Sandra with an opportunity to have a final, truly enjoyable meal with Thor and Lise who, like themselves, had opted for this Queensland extension. Oh, and of course, it also allowed Brian plenty of time to consider and assess his maritime experience of the past two weeks.

Well, when he got around to this, he started, like any good pessimist would, with what he considered to be the weak points of the experience, and the first of these was the fact that he and Sandra had not been able to board the *Caledonian Sky* in Worcester. This would have obviated the need to spend all that time in Hong Kong and that further time in Auckland, where they had felt that they had been doing little more than (metaphorically) treading water. However, bringing the *Caledonian Sky* up the Severn to be within fifteen miles of where Brian and Sandra lived would clearly have been a problem, as would the fact that it would then have been on the wrong side of the world to begin its transit of Melanesia. So maybe, thought Brian, he should move on to the second weak point, which had the added advantage of being a sensible point. And this was that the voyage through Melanesia had not been that rich in wildlife – especially for the fair-weather snorkellers in the party. There had been a few birds and some flying fish – and those remarkable pilot whales – but the observable local fauna generally comprised just one species, and this was the species called Homo sapiens. This was also the third weak point, in that no matter what effort had been made by its representatives in Melanesia, in the form of warlike welcomes or colourful ceremonies, one was always left with the feeling that one was watching a very much staged event. (Well, Brian was.) Of course, a more objective view might be that one was being given the opportunity to witness rare and disappearing cultures, and 'visits by white people from over the horizon' was a bloody good way of ensuring that the essence of these cultures was retained. But Brian thought objectivity was rather overrated, and as far as he was concerned, when it came to traditions, heritage and customs, there was just so much he could take, no matter how colourful or impenetrable they might be.

There was then the fourth weak point: the regimentation involved in shipping a cargo of eighty-eight middle-aged people around Melanesia and then constantly ferrying them to shore in small inflatables. It was all done very professionally and very efficiently, but too often Brian felt as though he was on a senior citizens' outing, organised and policed by a band of enthusiastic carers – otherwise known as the expedition team and its Zodiac drivers – and regarded by them as incapable of doing anything for himself. Furthermore, the regimentation – and the shepherding – became even more obvious when one was ashore, and it became increasingly difficult to remember that one was supposedly on an 'expedition'. Brian was quite sure that this wouldn't have been the sort of thing that Shackleton or indeed Captain Cook would have recognised as an expedition. Although, there again, they might have welcomed the air-conditioned buses…

OK. It was time for Brian to admit to himself that not only were the downsides of his recent trip no more than trivial quibbles but also that he was one very lucky bastard to have been able to make such a trip. Few could indulge themselves in such a manner, and most who could would not dwell on what was marginally wrong with the whole experience but instead on what was plainly right with it. In other words, it was about time that Brian moved on to the positive aspects of cruising through Melanesia. So he did.

The first real positive had a name. It was the MS *Caledonian Sky*. It was nothing less than an impeccable floating hotel, and what it offered in terms of service, comfort and food could not have been bettered. Except maybe by recruiting Sigourney Weaver to service the Bridge Deck cabins…

Yes, Brian and Sandra's experience of ships and boats was pretty limited, but they knew enough about seagoing vessels to realise that they don't come much better than the *Caledonian Sky*. In fact, it was so good on board this ship, that the second real positive for Brian was simply 'being on the ship' – as in spending days at sea with only the sea as the view. There was something magical about this experience – which he doubted ever emerged if one was in a life raft and starving to death, but which was there to absorb and to savour if one was fortunate enough to be on a craft such as the wonderful *Caledonian Sky*. In fact, Brian had wondered whether the operators of this vessel had ever considered putting on a cruise to nowhere, during which the *CS* would simply meander around the ocean keeping well away from any land of any sort and therefore the need to deploy those blasted inflatables or the need to tangle with any sort of anthropology or the like. He eventually concluded that they probably hadn't.

Anyway, it was time to move on to the next positive about the cruise – which was an indisputable contradiction. Because it was the islands that Brian and Sandra had been able to see, both as idyllic, tree-covered oases in the middle of a sparkling blue sea and as close-up encounters, where one could marvel at their unique vegetation and their 'light-impact occupation'. Because despite Brian's mean-minded assessment of all those expositions of traditional culture, he had been aware that those traditional ways of living were probably indefinitely sustainable and they didn't lead to the rapid trashing of the world which is now the norm in most other parts of the planet. Furthermore they shone a light on how people can live more or less happy and contented lives without a giant fridge-freezer, a furlong-wide TV, a barista-style espresso coffee machine and a collection of designer handbags. Most of the Melanesians Brian and Sandra had come across – and particularly those living in remote and isolated settlements – had seemed a pretty cheerful and sunny lot. And a great deal more cheerful and sunny than many one would encounter on one's travels back in Britain – or even in Mr Trump's not-quite-Great-Again-America.

That thought took Brian to his next real positive from this trip, which was the opportunity it provided to meet some really nice people on the ship itself. Not all the passengers were wonderful, and a handful of them were to be avoided at all costs. But most were affable and approachable and a few were more than this; they were ready-made friends. Thor and Lise and Paul and Lydia were definitely in this category, and although contact had been made only late on in the voyage, there was then Anton and Meg. It could be argued that sailing around Melanesia was a fairly roundabout way of meeting new nice people, but it did work and it did represent one of the very best aspects of this faraway cruise. It may even have helped in finally extinguishing that blasted melancholia – which had not made an appearance since Brian had left Melanesia. Or maybe that was just down to those limericks. They really had done the job.

And that was the final unexpected positive of being at sea for two weeks: the opportunity to compose fifty brand new limericks. And it was fifty, and not just forty-nine. Because, in between slandering the Hilton Hotel and then the whole of Cairns, Brian had still found time to compose that final, fiftieth limerick. And it was ready to present to Sandra just before their Melanesian quest reached its conclusion in the form of a flight back to Blighty. It was as follows:

There was a young man called Legrande
Who could pleasure himself on demand
But the pleasure, it ceased
When his member he greased
And the whole thing got well out of hand

Sandra did giggle – quite a lot. And Brian knew he'd nailed it. Subtlety combined with out-and-out obscenity

– at last. Yes, he'd be very happy to take this limerick home – and, at the same time leave his melancholia back in Melanesia.

Until, of course, it was needed again…

By the same author:

Brian's World Series

Brian on the Brahmaputra (with Sujan in the Sundarbans)
A Syria Situation
Sabah-taged
Cape Earth
Strip Pan Wrinkle (in Namibia and Botswana)
Crystal Balls and Moroccan Walls
Marmite, Bites and Noisy Nights (in Zambia)
The Country-cides of Namibia and Botswana
First Choose Your Congo
Absolutely Galápagos

The Renton Tenting Trilogy

Dumpiter
Ticklers
Lollipop

Light-bites

Eggshell in Scrambled Eggs
Crats
The A-Z of Stuff

www.davidfletcherbooks.co.uk